LARGE
PRINT
WORD SEARCH

1

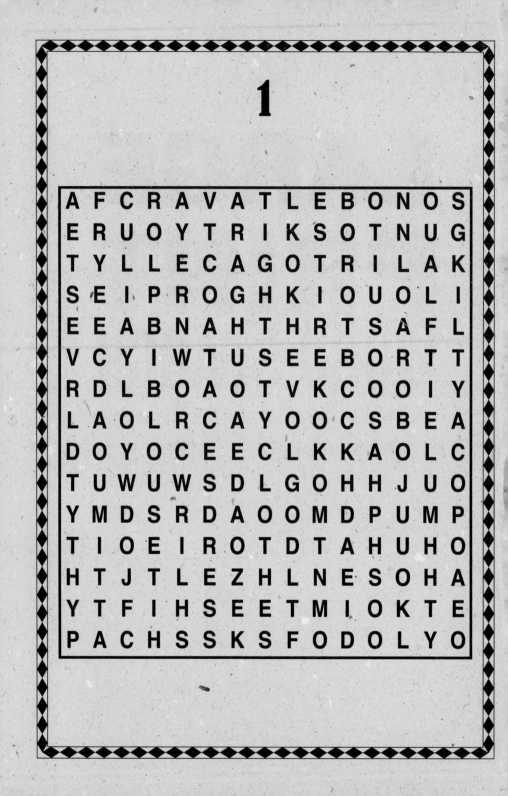

```
A F C R A V A T L E B O N O S
E R U O Y T R I K S O T N U G
T Y L L E C A G O T R I L A K
S E I P R O G H K I O U O L I
E E A B N A H T H R T S A F L
V C Y I W T U S E E B O R T T
R D L B O A O T V K C O O I Y
L A O L R C A Y O O C S B E A
D O Y O C E E C L K K A O L C
T U W U W S D L G O H H J U O
Y M D S R D A O O M D P U M P
T I O E I R O T D T A H U H O
H T J T L E Z H L N E S O H A
Y T F I H S E E T M I O K T E
P A C H S S K S F O D O L Y O
```

WHAT TO WEAR

BELT	DRESS	PUMP
BIB	FEZ	ROBE
BLOUSE	FROCK	SHIFT
BOA	GLOVE	SHIRT
BOOT	HABIT	SHOE
CAP	HAT	SKIRT
CAPE	HOOD	SUIT
CLOAK	HOSE	SWEATER
CLOTHES	JACKET	TIE
COAT	JERSEY	TIGHTS
COLLAR	KILT	TOGA
CRAVAT	MASK	VEIL
CROWN	MITT	VEST
DERBY	PANTS	

2

```
K E A D L E B O W G L E P A C
J R D B D M E M N A I P O E L
P A D A U T C O N N I D A O D
S T U F R R O I Y R E W R T G
C S I M A T N R G B P C I A S
H R L V S V G A O L O O M R C
I E I D E F R O L R R E E D I
E P W N F E T E S D P L A N N
F L T O G E N F A T M U J P G
R A I N B H O I I L E D A H G
M N V K D S O C A L S R L N T
G G E N O Z F L M P E R I N D
R E A U T R I V D U G G A E W
S H O N D S B G J A G L H D A
Y N T D E S Y I Z O P B T C E
```

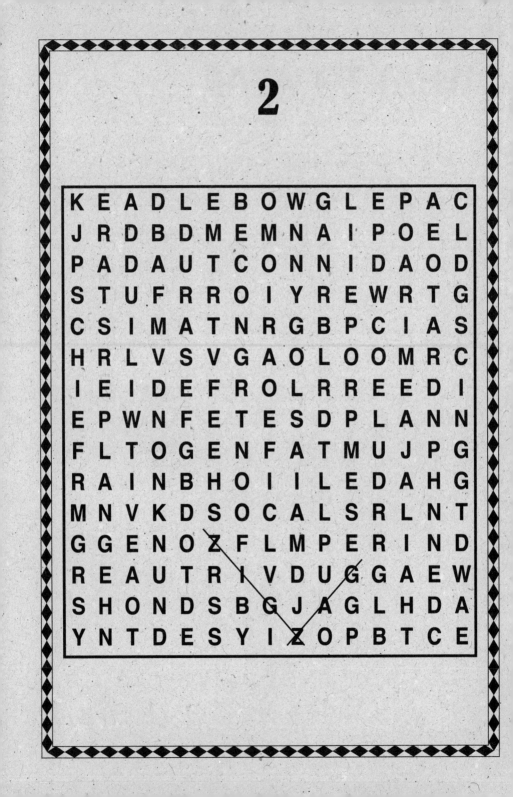

ZIGZAG

Instead of reading in a straight line, each entry has one bend in it. One word has been marked for you.

ADAPTIVE	GAME PLAN	ORDAIN
AGRIPPA	GEODESY	PERSUADE
BIFOCALS	HANDHOLD	RAINBOW
BOOTEE	INVENTIVE	SADDLEBOW
CARDIGAN	JOGGING	STAPLE
CEDARS	JUMP ROPE	THAILAND
CORSET	LEOTARD	TRADER
CRAVING	MAILED	UPLIFT
DEFROSTER	MEMOIR	VIRTUOSO
EGGPLANT	MISCHIEF	WIRING
FESTOON	NOCTURNAL	ZIGZAG
FLANGE	OOLOGY	

3

```
S P R E Z Z U B I L L E P S T
T O L G R M R O T S D R O W O
N T E A E O S R E T T E L K P
E S E S Y R C F E L Z Z U P K
M D O L E A S S R E W E I V C
G L E W B L T C E J B U S E A
E A S R A M N H Y E N O M G J
S N J N I K A N O Y A L P D Y
A I I H S F T R C M I D N E A
I F B A O H S A C V E I S L L
O I D U T S E S E S W M T W P
M M Q U E S T I O N D A N O D
R E S A E T N I A R B R I N R
L S S D N U O R H A C Y O K O
P U D E U L C W O H S P P W W
```

BRAINTEASER

(Based on the Channel 5 game show)

ANSWER
ASK
BRAINTEASER
BUZZER
CASH
CLUED UP
CONTESTANTS
CROSSFIRE
FINAL
HOST
JACKPOT
KNOWLEDGE
LETTERS

LIVE
LOSE
MONEY
PLAY AT HOME
PLAY ON
POINTS
PUZZLE
PYRAMID
QUESTION
ROUNDS
SCORE
SEGMENTS
SEMI FINAL

SHOW
SPELL
STOP
STUDIO
SUBJECT
VIEWERS
WIN
WORD PLAY
WORD
   SCRAMBLE
WORD STORM

4

```
T L Y G N I D R E B O S T
Y M A A W R E I T L P O K
R Y O R I B A L P L E E R
A M R O H T R R A I L T A
E U R O L A S I L T S O D
R R S N U G N U I A S N B
D D U G O T D R O T U A I
L M O C R M I I T I R S V
T U N D S N M N S D D A U
L H U F G B O O E M P E T
W L Y Y L T O M C I A R T
L Y D Y R A N I D R O L M
S O M B R E T D L A N A B
```

DON'T BE GLUM

BANAL

COMMON

DARK

DIM

DINGY

DISMAL

DRAB

DREARY

DULL

FLAT

GLOOM

HUMDRUM

INSIPID

OBSCURE

ORDINARY

PLAIN

ROUTINE

SOBER

SOMBRE

STALE

TEDIOUS

TIRING

USUAL

VAPID

5

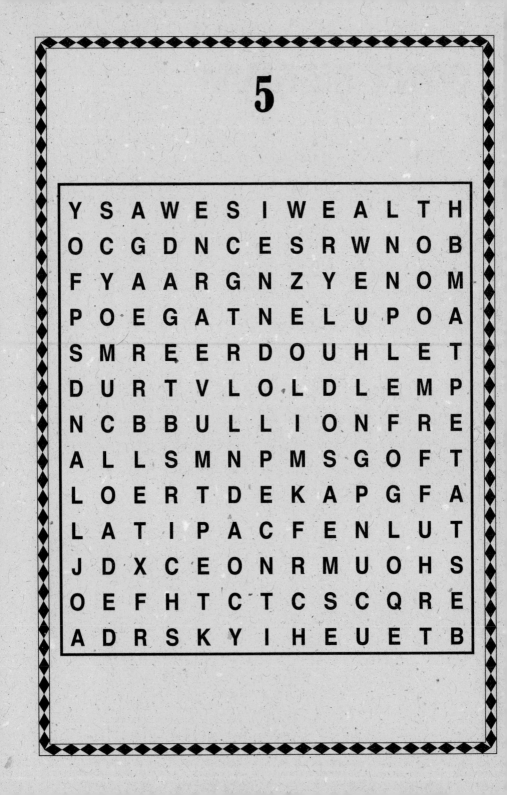

```
Y S A W E S I W E A L T H
O C G D N C E S R W N O B
F Y A A R G N Z Y E N O M
P O E G A T N E L U P O A
S M R E E R D O U H L E T
D U R T V L O L D L E M P
N C B B U L L I O N F R E
A L L S M N P M S G O F T
L O E R T D E K A P G F A
L A T I P A C F E N L U T
J D X C E O N R M U O H S
O E F H T C T C S C Q R E
A D R S K Y I H E U E T B
```

CAPITAL GAINS

ACREAGE

AFFLUENCE

BULLION

CAPITAL

ESTATE

FLUSH

FORTUNE

GOLD

LAND

LEGACY

LOADED

MANOR

MEANS

MONEY

OPULENT

PROPERTY

RICH

STOCK

SUBSTANCE

WEALTH

6

```
S Y A D H T R I B D I L M D B
A T R E M I T A T S C H O O L
M E H A K S G M E P A N R O K
T V C G S E A T A L M O N H R
S E P V I R U R I O F O I D O
I N Z N R N E F M O S N N L W
R I G I I N E V U Q E R G I T
H N A M T T N R I A C E W H A
C G W H I T S U N N O T E C C
E E O M R E F N N J N F E G E
N O E R A E Y W E N D A K A N
D O B S R U O H L E S U S L T
A M O N T H S T L H T T A O U
Y N W N Y R E T I R E D X V R
S Y T I R U T A M R S R A E Y
```

TIME AFTER TIME

AFTERNOON

AGEING

A LIFETIME

ANNIVERSARY

AT SCHOOL

AT WORK

BIRTHDAYS

CENTURY

CHILDHOOD

CHRISTMAS

DAYS

EASTER

EVENING

FOUR SEASONS

HOURS

LOVE

MARRIAGE

MATURITY

MILLENNIUM

MINUTES

MONTHS

MORNING

NEW YEAR

NIGHTS

NOON

PARENTHOOD

RETIRED

SECONDS

TEENS

TIME

WEEKS

WHITSUN

YEARS

7

```
S H S E B M T A H W L Y W L P
M A Y E T E A S Q U P O O F R
G E C R A U T N O D R O I U E
S N A R T R F S D T K N T E R
L E I N I T C Y H J D S S N Y
H L F H R F D H O E R E H T I
W O A Y T E I D F U H K L M F
R T I E R O M C G A L W N I Z
Y N E W Q U N J E N I L G O P
G D A L L R T Y D L I H D S W
S N I I L A R L L L T Y C S E
T K F W K E U L E I O A D E M
E E A E H O I F N R N V T L I
C L D T W E R G S T I W E N T
K N O V E R E H W O N W Q U I
```

NAME THAT TUNE

The words in the following grid are all
found in a hit film theme tune. Can you name it?
Song: _____

ALL	INTO	OTHER	UNLESS
AND	KNOW	SACRIFICE	WALK
CAN'T	LIE	SEARCH	WANT
DIE	LIFE	SEE	WHAT
DON'T	LIKE	SOUL	WILL
DYING	LOOK	TAKE	WIRE
EYES	LOVE	TELL	WORTH
FIGHTING	MEAN	THERE	WOULD
FIND	MORE	TIME	YEAH
FOR	NOTHING	TRUE	YOU'LL
HEART	NOWHERE	TRYING	YOUR

8

```
Z S T A X S M R O G N R I A C
V I A B K C O T N A U Q U V H
S V F N O R A J N A M I L I K
D E A R Y K C O R T T I P N G
L N R E K A E P S E K I P T S
O N A V A K N E S E D N A A A
W E A L L S R T A N K O O C Y
S B E A T E S B E T K J C H A
T O K M V N E M N L L N N I L
O T H E I G E R E O A A O L A
C A M T C Y N P N L D S S T M
Q B U R A L E R B W P W B E I
F L I N D E R S D L F O O R H
E E I G I R Y N A G O L R N P
X O N N E L P E N N I N E S S
```

HIGH TIMES

ALPS	ELK	PENTLAND
ANDES	ETNA	PIKE'S PEAK
ARAFAT	EVEREST	PYRENEES
ATHOS	FLINDERS	QUANTOCK
ATLAS	HIMALAYAS	RIGI
BEN NEVIS	KEA	ROBSON
BLANC	KILIMANJARO	ROCKY
CAIRNGORMS	LENNOX	SNOWDON
CHILTERNS	LOGAN	TABLE
COOK	MALVERN	URAL
COTSWOLDS	MENDIP	VINTA
EIGER	PENNINES	

9

```
S A V A G E E T C T K F A
T L U C C O T R P O Y B B
M O R B I D R E G K N E C
A F I H N R N Y C O I D H
C F W A B I Z A R R E L A
A B D F D E W M E W U A N
B E E I E W A E T O A M S
R A T E P L H S I R A G I
E T N N R K I N K Y D D C
N E U D A M G I N E A N O
A R A I W N Y C M W W O O
R A H S I L U O H G S U D
E S I H E G N A R T S W L
```

HOW BIZARRE!

ABNORMAL

ASKEW

AWRY

BEDLAM

BIZARRE

DEMON

EERIE

ENIGMA

FIENDISH

GARISH

GHOULISH

GORY

HAUNTED

INEPT

KINKY

MACABRE

MORBID

OCCULT

OFF BEAT

OGRE

SAVAGE

STRANGE

WACKY

WARPED

WEIRD

10

```
E C N E R E F E R P T S N
V L L I W T A M I P T O O
I O E F B R M C O G I T I
T T I C Y A K L J T E S T
A P T C F L T U H N M C
N E O Y E I S L S V I N E
R C S D N N O D O O M W L
E C T K A S I N E T R O E
T A N E E V G L C E E D S
L H L R I G T D C L T N S
A G T D R T B T H E E R C
L R E F E E D I C E D U R
N H D S N O I T P O N T R
```

CAST A VOTE

ACCEPT   OPTIONS

ADOPT   PICK

ALTERNATIVE   POLL

AT WILL   PREFERENCE

BALLOT   RESOLUTION

DECIDE   SELECTION

DECLINE   SETTLE

DETERMINE   TURN DOWN

DIVIDE   VOICE

ELECTION   VOTE

GLEAN

```
P O U N D S V G N I L L I H S
I N O E M U E A B O D R O C U
A I K A R I L Q U A R T E R C
S C R R E N O E L I A W U U R
T K A I W Y U A N I N O A Z E
E E M P F R A N C O O N M E O
R L T M G U I L D E R I H I D
I I S E I P N E Y L K K C R U
Y N O L Y I R A L L O D A O C
A A B E T A T E S E P S R U S
L H I U O H K Y A T E I D U E
T G E B L S K L A Z T E U Q L
H F L M Z I E D R U O G P I B
A A I P I K L P N O L O C U U
B R A N I D I R H A M D N A R
```

FOREIGN CURRENCY

AFGHANI	KRONA	QUARTER
BAHT	KRONE	QUETZAL
BALBOA	KYAT	RAND
COLON	LEK	RIYAL
CORDOBA	LEMPIRA	RUBLE
CRUZEIRO	LEONE	RUPEE
DIME	LEU	RUPIAH
DINAR	LEV	SHILLING
DIRHAM	LIRA	SOL
DOLLAR	MARK	SUCRE
DRACHMA	NICKEL	WON
ESCUDO	OSTMARK	YEN
FRANC	PESETA	YUAN
GOURDE	PESO	ZLOTY
GUILDER	PIASTER	
KIP	POUNDS	

12

```
T T C C A Y L L I H P R E A C
B E R I H S E H C G H D R D G
E R O O W E E N O M E L L O W
U E W S F I D R N E A O P L D
L Y D A R E G D X I W D O Z E
B U I B G O U D A S V W E L Y
H R E N N L E Q E R F E A F T
S G I Z A G O M O A O D U N R
I T O C A S Y U T R Y E O L E
N L R T O L E I C E S T E R B
A I T O C T U M L E L F U N M
D O V J N Q T S R I S T E I E
C A B O C G N A T A A T L T M
K F Y B R E D S L M P D E C A
C R E D W I N D S O R B M R C
```

CHEESY FEAT

BLUE VINNEY	EDAM	MILD
BRIE	FETA	PARMESAN
CABOC	GLOUCESTER	RED WINDSOR
CAERPHILLY	GORGONZOLA	RICOTTA
CAMEMBERT	GOUDA	ROQUEFORT
CHEDDAR	GRUYERE	STILTON
CHESHIRE	LEICESTER	STRONG
COTTAGE	LOW-FAT	WENSLEYDALE
CROWDIE	LYMESWOLD	
DANISH BLUE	MATURE	
DERBY	MELLOW	

13

```
E C L A I R E C I R O U Q I L
N T A M R A G U S Y E L R A B
B U E R U T X I M Y L L O D J
I N E T A L O C O H C P L E L
W O L L A M H S R A M E L E L
K L I M G L E T N O M L T F A
K Y T I U R F L E O Y C N F B
P P M A B G P V N B B H I O D
E O A F M E R A A Q R N M T E
A P R Y U F G B S N K E O S E
R I Z D H D I N O T I C H B S
D L I N D E G U A M I L O S I
R L P A S I G E U R I L L R N
O O A C J A C G P M O E L A A
P L N D T S N A E B Y L L E J
```

SWEET TREAT

ACID DROP
ANISEED BALL
APRICOT
BARLEY SUGAR
BONBON
CANDY
CARAMEL
CHOCOLATE
DOLLY MIXTURE
ÉCLAIR
FRUITY
FUDGE

GUM
HUMBUG
JELLY BABIES
JELLY BEANS
LEMON
LIME
LIQUORICE
LOLLIPOP
MARSHMALLOW
MARZIPAN
MILK
MINT

NOUGAT
NUT
ORANGE
PASTILLE
PEAR DROP
ROCK
SHERBET
TOFFEE
VANILLA

14

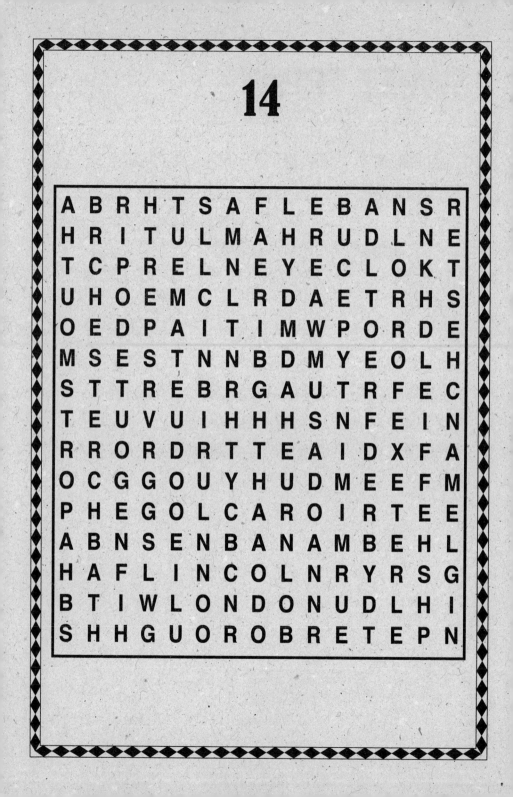

```
A B R H T S A F L E B A N S R
H R I T U L M A H R U D L N E
T C P R E L N E Y E C L O K T
U H O E M C L R D A E T R H S
O E D P A I T I M W P O R D E
M S E S T N N B D M Y E O L H
S T T R E B R G A U T R F E C
T E U V U I H H H S N F E I N
R R O R D R T T E A I D X F A
O C G G O U Y H U D M E E F M
P H E G O L C A R O I R T E E
A B N S E N B A N A M B E H L
H A F L I N C O L N R Y R S G
B T I W L O N D O N U D L H I
S H H G U O R O B R E T E P N
```

IN THE CITY

BANGOR	EDINBURGH	PETERBOROUGH
BATH	ELGIN	PLYMOUTH
BELFAST	ELY	PORTSMOUTH
BIRMINGHAM	EXETER	SHEFFIELD
CAMBRIDGE	HULL	SOUTHAMPTON
CARDIFF	LANCASTER	TRURO
CHESTER	LEEDS	WELLS
COVENTRY	LINCOLN	WINCHESTER
DERBY	LONDON	YORK
DUNDEE	MANCHESTER	
DURHAM	PERTH	

15

```
P A U S D N A H E K A H S
N C E E R F S L F F E N T
N R T L D E Y P R O O R R
G O E D F T W I E O O E E
E C I N R U E O L E M D A
T C R A N N N L L E C T M
A A P C D I A Y M F F H E
R S F S O B D B T E C R R
B I T N E S E R P P A H S
E O E F S R K N O H R S C
L N S C I S A N S K D E H
E S D O H G C S T C M L R
C O N G R A T U L A T E E
```

PARTY TIME

BALLOONS	GIFT
CAKE	OCCASION
CANDLES	PARTY
CARD	PRESENT
CELEBRATE	REMEMBER
CONGRATULATE	SHAKE HANDS
DINNER	SHARE
FLOWERS	SPEECH
FOOD	STREAMERS
FRIENDS	
FUN	

16

```
A C T K R E S S E R I A N O C
B I F R I A A E R O F L O T I
R P N O A D B S P A E R S O T
I M G N N E E E Y F I E A H N
T Y U W A L N C I J W L K C A
I L L I Y T A N X H E I A R L
S O F L R A I A T G L T D A T
H W A I D N I R I A O U S N A
A G I V B U O F B N G N A O N
I N R S S N M R L Y A P T M I
R E H A S E V I J H N F N A G
W M I T L A M A T D A N A I R
A R I A N N I F R O I S Q T I
Y H L B O Q U R A I R E B I V
S U G N I L R E A C G C L R D
```

AIRLINES

AER LINGUS	EL AL	RYANAIR
AEROFLOT	FINNAIR	SABENA
AIR FRANCE	GULF AIR	SWISSAIR
AIR INDIA	IBERIA	US AIR
ALIA	LOGANAIR	VARIG
BRITANNIA	LUFTHANSA	VIRGIN
BRITISH AIR-WAYS	MONARCH	ATLANTIC
CONAIR	NORTHWEST	
DAN-AIR	OLYMPIC	
DELTA	QANTAS	
EASY JET		

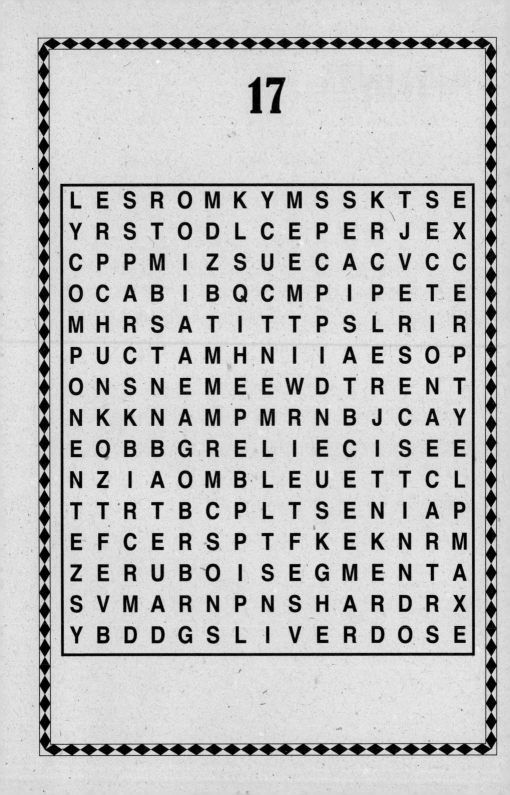

```
L E S R O M K Y M S S K T S E
Y R S T O D L C E P E R J E X
C P P M I Z S U E C A C V C C
O C A B I B Q C M P I P E T E
M H R S A T I T T P S L R I R
P U C T A M H N I I A E S O P
O N S N E M E E W D T R E N T
N K K N A M P M R N B J C A Y
E Q B B G R E L I E C I S E E
N Z I A O M B L E U E T T C L
T T R T B C P L T S E N I A P
E F C E R S P T F K E K N R M
Z E R U B O I S E G M E N T A
S V M A R N P N S H A R D R X
Y B D D G S L I V E R D O S E
```

FRAGMENTED

BITE	LUMP	SHARD
BITS	MEMBER	SLICE
BRANCH	MORSEL	SLIVER
CHUNK	NITS	SMITHEREEN
COMPONENT	PARCEL	SPECIMEN
CRUMB	PART	SPECK
CUTTING	PIECES	SPLINTER
DABS	PORTION	TABS
DOSE	SAMPLE	TASTE
DOTS	SCRAP	TIDBIT
DROP	SECTION	TRACE
EXAMPLE	SECTOR	VERSE
EXCERPT	SEEDS	WISP
FRAGMENT	SEGMENT	

18

```
G D G R I L L H E L B M U R G
G R A T E H H G R E E N G R R
R D A S G R A V E H G F A H O
A H G M G F Y V A R G P G R U
N W E G M H W F G G E H G H N
D G G G R A N N Y S S R R W D
F R S R F G R A F F I T I G H
E A S A E G H E D G R A D E E
F Z A P G G T Y G R E A T G G
F E R H H A G H K A J D H R Y
E F G R U N T G G S N E H I D
I S G D F H J R H P G A H T E
R G A D G R E E K S D G O H E
G R O V E G S Y S S O R G R R
G J G S S D H D H Y P M U R G
```

IT'S 'GR'EAT

GRADE	GRAVE	GRIT
GRADUATE	GRAVY	GROAN
GRAFFITI	GRAZE	GROSS
GRAMMAR	GREAT	GROUND
GRAND	GREEDY	GROVE
GRANNY	GREEK	GRUMBLE
GRAPES	GREEN	GRUMPY
GRAPH	GREY	GRUNT
GRASP	GRID	
GRASS	GRIEF	
GRATE	GRILL	

19

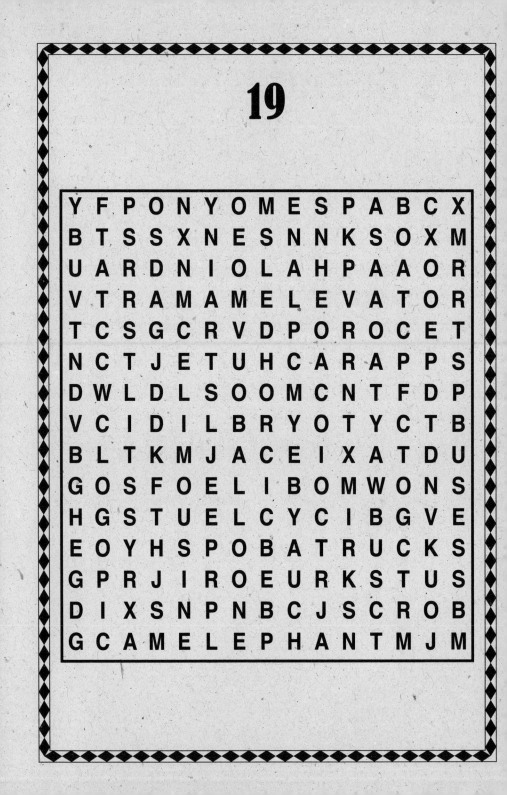

```
Y F P O N Y O M E S P A B C X
B T S S X N E S N N K S O X M
U A R D N I O L A H P A A O R
V T R A M A M E L E V A T O R
T C S G C R V D P O R O C E T
N C T J E T U H C A R A P P S
D W L D L S O O M C N T F D P
V C I D I L B R Y O T Y C T B
B L T K M J A C E I X A T D U
G O S F O E L I B O M W O N S
H G S T U E L C Y C I B G V E
E O Y H S P O B A T R U C K S
G P R J I R O E U R K S T U S
D I X S N P N B C J S C R O B
G C A M E L E P H A N T M J M
```

ON THE MOVE

BALLOON	JEEP	SLED
BARGE	JET	SNOWMOBILE
BICYCLE	LIMOUSINE	STILTS
BOAT	MOTORCYCLE	SUBWAY
BUSES	PARACHUTE	TAXI
CAMEL	PLANE	TRACTOR
CANOE	POGO	TRAIN
CARS	PONY	TRAM
ELEPHANT	RAFT	TROLLEY
ELEVATOR	SHIP	TRUCK
GLIDER	SKATES	TUBE
HORSE	SKIS	VANS

20

```
L O S S A M I L A D B I S N E
G Y W T A N G I E R R O R R L
I S B D A S C H B G E N O A N
B I A R Y N D E K L S A T O Z
R D M N E D A I N O T U T A G
A A L L C M N H E C A P E A R
L C A P S V E T G L M E R L U
T V P I O J E R A A A N D E O
A F G R E B N E H T O G A X B
R A B A R M E T N A R Z M A R
E U L E Z E U S E E V M E N E
D N O U S O C Y P P R E U D H
S W I S S S E D O H R R N R C
U L U L O N O H C N O B S I L
K A T T E L L A V S I A L A C
```

PORTS OF CALL

ADEN	GOTHENBERG
ALEXANDRIA	HONOLULU
BREMERHAVEN	LIMASSOL
BREST	LISBON
CADIS	PALMA
CALAIS	PIRAEUS
CHERBOURG	RHODES
COPENHAGEN	ROTTERDAM
DUBROVNIK	SOUTHAMPTON
GENOA	SUEZ
GIBRALTAR	TANGIER

21

```
E R A W D R A H F B M E S S A G E S
P R O G R A M A R I S K A D E I R C
U O U E P I T E D U N E N I L N O I
K T T C H A T R O O M A R R I P Y H
C I P R D U E M N F W N N E A U R P
A N U E P Q O D O Y J N O C M T O A
B O T M J F D R I V E R L T E P M R
A M O M E W O R T W I N D O W S E G
T C K O G N C R A U D X F R A T M R
E T A C I N U M M O C L E Y N D E R
D M E E L I F Q R A B N R I U S C E
U A V N C U R S O R T Y R O W Q G S
C T I E R A W T F O S P E O W A A E
A C A C H E H M N D H M R K P L M A
T W E B S I T E I V A B O E Z T E R
I L S N T C E N N O C O M D I F S C
O L O G O N G S I M F O L D E R S H
N Y D B G N I P P O H S E N T M R D
```

SURF'S UP

BACKUP	FILE	MENU
BROWSER	FINANCE	MESSAGES
CACHE	FOLDERS	MODEM
CHATROOM	FORMAT	MONITOR
COMMUNICATE	GAMES	MOUSE
COMPUTER	GRAPHICS	ONLINE
CONNECT	HARDWARE	OUTPUT
CURSOR	HOME PAGE	PRINTER
DATA	INFORMATION	PROGRAM
DIRECTORY	INPUT	RESEARCH
DOWNLOAD	INTERNET	SHOPPING
DRIVER	KEYBOARD	SOFTWARE
E-COMMERCE	LOAD	WEBSITE
EDIT	LOG ON	WINDOWS
EDUCATION	MAT	WORLD WIDE
E-MAIL	MEMORY	

22

```
B I L R N A P R E T E P L O S
R P L R E L B A S H F U L S T
S E I G R Y A G A R F I E L D
K E P N W S E D A R V H S B C
O H E S K O N P Y E C T A O H
O G L R A P M R O U Y M T L A
H R M E F C A Y D P B U N N R
N U E P H L L N O I L N O A L
I M R M A G O O T P A D H H I
A P F U P Y N W I H U O A K E
T Y U H P S E H E M E C C E B
P R D T Y R C P B R T R O R R
A Y D N E W H O O L A B P E O
C O T I H C N A P D A L E H W
T R E S U O M Y E K C I M S N
```

CARTOON TIME

The words in the following grid are all cartoon characters.

BALOO

BAMBI

BASHFUL

CAPTAIN HOOK

CASPER

CHARLIE
  BROWN

CHIP

DALE

DOC

DOPEY

DUCHESS

DUMBO

ELMER FUDD

FLOWER

GARFIELD

GRUMPY

HAPPY

LADY

MICKEY
  MOUSE

MOWGLI

MR MAGOO

OLIVE OYL

PANCHITO

PETER PAN

PINK PANTHER

PLUTO

POCAHONTAS

POPEYE

SHERE KHAN

SNOOPY

THUMPER

WENDY

23

```
A S H B Y D E L A Z O U C N A
Z Z E P O R T E O Z C J C T E
G A Z G I Z Z A N Z A N F O Z
Z R A R R E H T I Z I M Y L O
E E E Z B Z E R O Z D G E A M
L B R R O P C A E N O Z T E B
E A A H Z O O M P L Z H O Z I
M Z O T N S M C O Y Z O G R E
E P E I R U S O Z Z O Z Y Z P
N Z U N Z Z Z R Z O H Z I Z
O M R E A Y L T P P Z Z R Z
Z Z B Z Y N A Z Z E H Z Z C K
G U Z Z Y E A Z Z Z Y I Z O N
Z Z A I Z Z T S E Z T O C N O
A Z L I Z Z A B E T E N Z Z Z
```

Z WORDS

ZANY	ZIGZAG	ZOO
ZAREBA	ZINC	ZOOLOGY
ZEAL	ZION	ZOOM
ZEALOT	ZIP	ZOOMORPHIC
ZEBRA	ZIRCON	ZOOPHYTE
ZEBU	ZIRCONIUM	ZYGOTE
ZENANA	ZITHER	
ZENITH	ZODIAC	
ZEPHYR	ZOETROPE	
ZERO	ZOMBIE	
ZEST	ZONE	

24

```
S T N I A R T S E R B I K
T H K H S E V Y G R R I C
E S A D G B J N A O R H B
L N G C P R G C N O A L C
T A B N K R E R N I L K A
S P O L I L I S N L K H P
I S N J E N E S T G J N T
R F D T G L E S O R F H I
W M S S C C P T G N I J V
A E D A A M J H S X E C I
P T N R A D G J N A C R T
P A B L S R E T T E F H Y
M L C F S F F U C D N A H
```

BONDING

BONDS

BRACELETS

BRACES

CAPTIVITY

CHAINS

CLAMPS

FASTENINGS

FETTERS

HANDCUFFS

IRON RINGS

IRONS

MANACLES

METAL

PRISONER

RESTRAINTS

RESTRICT

SHACKLES

SNAPS

WRISTLETS

25

```
T U L D A L L I H C N I H C A
T G I U O G N I M M E L E K K
A O B W Q R E V A E B N A I M
R P R M H T M T V U I N L N G
A H E B A A A O O P G S T I K
B E G N U R I R U A U E P H N
Y R S T D E M C R S L A D H U
P N I U G L R O H E E Y L A M
A D O C O O O Y T N T E C M P
C L A O P M D P I R R A S S I
C E K T O S Y U G R E H W T H
G I T U V I G N I I R E B E C
O F S C O S D U I E A N R R W
P E R O L A Q H W P L N T A R
H A R V E S T M O U S E T L T
```

RODENT RAGE

Can you find the 26 types of rodent in the list?

CAPYBARA

CHINCHILLA

CHIPMUNK

CLOUD RAT

COYPU

DEGU

DORMOUSE

FIELD/VOLE

GERBIL

GIANT/
  BEAVER

GOPHER

GUINEA PIG

HAMSTER

HARVEST
  MOUSE

KANGAROO
  MOUSE

LEMMING

MARMOT

MOLE RAT

PORCUPINE

SHREW

SPINY MOUSE

SQUIRREL

SUSLIK

TREE RAT

TUCO-TUCO

WATER RAT

26

```
C O M E D I A N R E L G G U J
N A M M R O F R E P Z F D J G
O B L U K I N T E R V A L H I
I E R T A E H T V O W D K S H
T C N S C R O W D G C E T I M
I D O O S C E N E R Y N L N N
D A N C E H G T U A E B V G E
U P P E J O A S D M Q S A E T
A P Q U R R T R U M X H R R S
O L O S I U S R E E P O I O I
E A F G H S T R T S C W E S T
M U S I C S Y R T N Y A T U R
Z S F I N A L E E Y Z A Y V A
A E N I A T R U C V R X N W Y
B C A R T S E H C R O D H T J
```

THE ENTERTAINERS

APPLAUSE   FINALE   SINGER

ARTISTE   INSTRUMENT   SOLO

AUDITION   INTERVAL   STAGE

CHORUS   JUGGLER   STAR

COMEDIAN   MUSIC   THEATRE

COSTUME   ORCHESTRA   VARIETY

CROWD   OVERTURE

CURTAIN   PERFORM

DANCE   PROGRAMME

DUET   SCENERY

ENCORE   SHOW

27

```
G H S N A I G O L O E H T F D
W A I M C S M D S E S N I S A
T V R Q U I R I I R K S N I B
O R C D N S N E E V H U L A E
W H A E E G I G D E A I L R N
E S R V E N N C R L C D D E I
R S R R E E E M I E I O G H T
D V S E S L E R C A C U A P S
N M K S K N L S S T N Y B O U
A V E A W A R E O N R S R T G
B M D F H E M R R O M K I S U
C A M T Y V S E G S B O E I A
M B R W H S T E O P N O L R Y
Z A A R A B R A B H J C B H S
M L K U Q G R N I P S I R C V
```

WHAT A SAINT

The words in the following grid are all saints and what they are the patron saint of. Can you match the pairs?

ADAM	DAVID	MESSENGERS
ANDREW	DOCTORS	MINERS
ANNE	FISHERMEN	MUSICIANS
AUGUSTINE	GABRIEL	POETS
BARBARA	GARDENERS	SHOEMAKERS
BUILDERS	GREGORY	SINGERS
CECILIA	IVO	THEOLOGIANS
CHRISTOPHER	LAWYERS	TRAVELLERS
COOKS	LUKE	
CRISPIN	MARTHA	

28

```
L G U E S S I R S Y T T S
A P E S W N C A E S P E L
D L L T S T H E C S A S Y
N L I I A T A H R V N O S
A R D B I V T N E T S I L
C E E B E C I S T P A O L
S T T P R L D R O Y D N A
N I N F O R M O P N H M T
T E N E O R C S E E I U E
I H W P O S T U R T O L S
P I O S O G N S E A S O T
Y C I U J N Y M T R T C U
G O S S I P H O T O S S U
```

IT'S A SCANDAL

CHAT	LATEST	STARS
COLUMN	LIBEL	TITBIT
EAVESDROP	LISTEN	
GOSSIP	NEWS	
GUESS	PHOTOS	
HEAR	PRIVATE	
INFORM	REPORTS	
INNUENDO	SCANDAL	
INSIDE	SCOOP	
ITEM	SECRET	
JUICY	SPY	

29

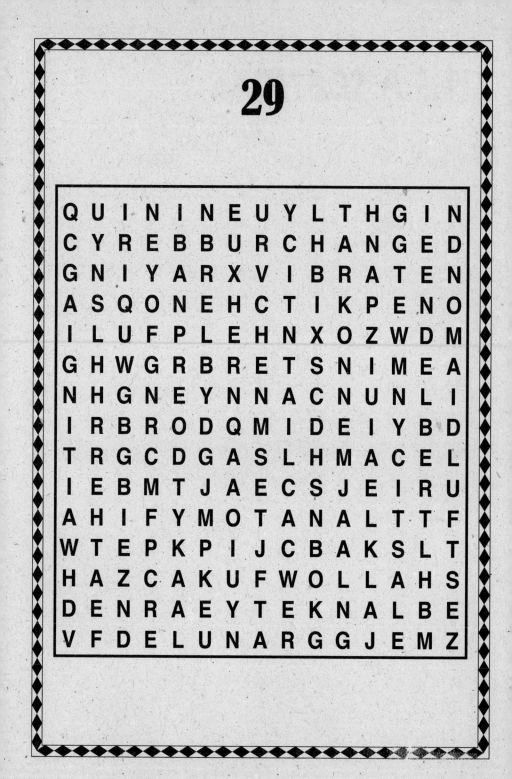

```
Q U I N I N E U Y L T H G I N
C Y R E B B U R C H A N G E D
G N I Y A R X V I B R A T E N
A S Q O N E H C T I K P E N O
I L U F P L E H N X O Z W D M
G H W G R B R E T S N I M E A
N H G N E Y N N A C N U N L I
I R B R O D Q M I D E I Y B D
T R G C D G A S L H M A C E L
I E B M T J A E C S J E I R U
A H I F Y M O T A N A L T T F
W T E P K P I J C B A K S L T
H A Z C A K U F W O L L A H S
D E N R A E Y T E K N A L B E
V F D E L U N A R G G J E M Z
```

ALPHABETICAL

ANATOMY	LEOPARD	WAITING
BLANKET	MINSTER	X-RAYING
CHANGED	NIGHTLY	YEARNED
DIAMOND	OCTAGON	ZESTFUL
ELASTIC	PYJAMAS	
FEATHER	QUININE	
GRANULE	RUBBERY	
HELPFUL	SHALLOW	
ICEBERG	TREBLED	
JASMINE	UNCANNY	
KITCHEN	VIBRATE	

30

```
L W O B R A G U S S P O O N G
Y R E K C O R C Z T T N F I F
E F I N K V S I N K O A R P O
R E L O R E S S A C R P E G R
E D A Y Q N R D S H A E M N K
C N T O P E E F F O C C A I R
U A E D Y T D P C R K U E L E
A T I B R X N I E P H A T L X
S S G A E O K A L I B S S O I
H E Y C L E M A P E E L E R M
E K F C T J T A N W S S A L G
L A M T U E A L U T A P S E U
B C L G C P L D P U C G G E M
A E I E K H S I D E S E E H C
T H V T A O B Y V A R G U C J
```

DINNER TIME

CAKE STAND	GLASS	RACK
CASSEROLE	GRAVY BOAT	ROLLING PIN
CHAIR	KETTLE	SAUCEPAN
CHEESE DISH	KNIFE	SAUCER
COFFEE POT	LID	SINK
CREAM JUG	MIXER	SPATULA
CROCKERY	MUG	SPOON
CUP	OVEN	STEAMER
CUTLERY	PAN	SUGAR BOWL
DISH	PEELER	TABLE
EGG CUP	PLATE	TRAY
FORK	POT	

```
W L E L N Y R O P C R A P E C
I N B A A V E S L E G O F F I
G E S E T C V T D I N V N D A
L A S S I E I L E T R E E D P
A P O R O L C T L S O L D E R
P N W B N L O S A E P O T T E
E T A O S T O F P E T C E I A
R S G P X O I F A F S L L L M
P O E D B B C E T I R A A I R
A T S R O D T S Y W S S N A M
M P C A A R I C K I N D O S T
L L I P E V D E N E W O P E R
A S E E L N E L V E L O E W A
R X C P O L A A E S E P L I C
B O O N D C S S F R A G I T H
```

MAIL TRAIL

Starting at the letter (L) move up, down, left or right to find the mail items listed below. Not listed at the end of the trail are items that need careful wrapping when sent through the post.

Fragile items: _____

AIRMAIL LETTER

BROWN PAPER

CARDBOARD BOX

DELIVERY VAN

FIRST CLASS

FRAGILE WITH CARE

LABEL

LAST COLLECTION

PADDED ENVELOPE

PARCEL POST

PILLAR BOX

POSTAGE STAMP

POSTMAN

POST OFFICE

SEALED ENVELOPE

SECOND CLASS

SORTING OFFICE

STICKY TAPE

WINDOW ENVELOPE

32

```
N O T T O C M L N N B T V C N
O P S A N E R O U E P A I O M
T R B K G O T O D B R I T O N
R O F A E P T L T K U T T O Y
A T T O Y L I S R O U T S O N
C O O R K N E A I M N F T O N
N N K S G B I T T P O D T O H
O A U T O M A T O N T S N G N
T P O I N T Z D N N E X O O O
E N N L O Q H E M L L G T L T
L N O T T U L G R I G K L M U
P B T O X F S A W J N M I U O
M R U N E T H N M A I T W T R
I N F C S C D S L R S E O O C
S N O T E A H P M E L T O N P
```

...TON

The words in the following grid all end 'TON'.

AUTOMATON	FUTON	PROTON
BADMINTON	GLUTTON	SEXTON
BATON	KRYPTON	SIMPLETON
BEDLINGTON	MEGATON	SINGLETON
BRITON	MELTON	SKELETON
BUTTON	MUTON	STILTON
CARTON	MUTTON	TRITON
CHARLESTON	PHAETON	WILTON
COTTON	PISTON	
CROTON	PITON	
CROUTON	PLANKTON	

33

```
O E I S A E P E E W S P U
S S I O E E P U O T H I C
I E G Y A R P S W R A E U
D W S I E A I N M W M E R
R I L O W I E I E A P T L
A F R O T B R M Y S O A E
E I U U S T I A I E O O R
B Y C I E S R T I G U G S
I E D W K G S I S C R U B
S T I C W H I V I B I E U
I P O M A D E I S O M J Y
I L W V R U O D A P M O P
I E E I S O S D I A R B C
```

HAIR CARE

AFRO	POMADE
BEARD	POMPADOUR
BRAIDS	SCRUB
COMB	SHAMPOO
CURLERS	SHAVE
CURLS	SPRAY
CUT	TOUPEE
DYE	TRIM
GOATEE	UPSWEEP
GREY	VITAMINS
LOCKS	WIGS

34

N	R	I	S	T	H	L	A	R	I	M	D	A
O	G	E	N	E	R	A	L	T	I	E	M	F
W	O	R	V	A	L	G	T	N	U	O	C	R
S	F	O	B	E	O	N	O	R	A	B	O	E
K	E	B	D	N	R	E	N	R	T	N	O	C
I	I	N	C	S	O	E	O	M	R	D	E	I
N	H	T	A	E	S	S	N	E	O	U	R	F
G	C	O	G	T	S	E	V	D	Y	K	O	F
T	A	D	I	E	O	O	C	D	A	E	T	O
H	U	O	F	T	G	R	F	N	M	H	C	E
J	I	O	R	N	E	E	U	Q	I	P	O	A
E	R	T	Y	O	F	A	T	H	E	R	D	M
P	H	S	I	W	R	E	I	M	E	R	P	R

WHO'S IN CHARGE?

ADMIRAL

BARON

CHIEF

COUNT

DOCTOR

DUKE

FATHER

GENERAL

GOVERNOR

JUDGE

KING

MAYOR

OFFICER

PREMIER

PRINCESS

PROFESSOR

QUEEN

RABBI

REVEREND

SENATOR

35

```
H O R U O S D N A T E E W S M
O S C R A N B E R R Y J O I B
O D I S T E L P P A P T N A W
A T A D A M U L P R A T R H C
L R S E A B O R O M R B Y H E
A U M E R R A V O E E E E L T
S E A O P B E T T C L E L E T
A S E T O N A S U S S E O M E
M S R H C R E E R E M Y Y A R
A A C A T C H A N O W R S H G
K H L A R O P S N T H R T C I
K C R O Y Y O S U N I U E E A
I E W S A T A Y R M T C R B N
T R I S B L A C K B E A N L I
G N F E S I A D N A L L O H V
```

SO SAUCY!

The words in the following grid are all sauces.

APPLE

BARBECUE

BECHAMEL

BLACK BEAN

BREAD

CHASSEUR

CHEESE

CRANBERRY

CREAM

CURRY

HOLLANDAISE

HORSERADISH

HOY SIN

LEMON

MINT

MUSHROOM

OYSTER

PARSLEY

PESTO

PLUM

PROVENCAL

SATAY

SOY

SWEET AND
SOUR

TABASCO

TARTAR

TIKKA MASALA

TOMATO

VINAIGRETTE

WHITE

WORCESTER

36

```
E L D D A S R E D D U H S
A B I D D E R F L I Y A C
P A D D L E G N I D D U B
L A G D K R G E L D D I M
S Q D N E T H N E L A I F
G O U D I A G N I E C P R
T W D G E D E L D D U M G
H A E U N D D O A D D N P
L I L D E I M A D D I I D
R J D L D T D L L D D N K
M U D D Y I E D D C I E L
I D A V E O N U E W X T N
A S W B T N P G Y B O E Y
```

DOUBLE UP

ADDITION

ADDLED

BEDDING

BIDDER

BUDDING

CADDY

CLADDING

DIDDLED

GLADDEN

HIDDEN

KIDDING

LADDER

MIDDLE

MUDDLED

MUDDY

ODDITY

PADDED

PADDLE

PUDDING

PUDDLE

RIDDLE

SADDENED

SADDLE

SHUDDER

TODDLER

WADDLED

WEDDING

37

```
L D S A S A L U T E S E Y L Y
E C R M N A Q T M L L M A R R
G T R A R E T A R T R N A O T
I U A E F A R E T A E T J X N
O P N V W T E A M S I A R Y A
N E M I I O B R R L M N O T F
G C V A T R P A I Z E S C N N
C R L R C S P M Z F N H K A I
A O S R E C I F F O M A E T Q
V F P U O C F T I L O J T U S
A F Q N D A R S G K A K S J P
L B V R T O I U B R I G A D E
R O I S O V A R I F L E Z A A
Y L S P I R K N A T O I D A R
L D S D D F R E L I S S I M S
```

BATTLE GROUND

ADJUTANT	DRILL	POWER
ARENA	FIREARMS	PRIVATE
ARMY	FLAG	RADIO
ARSENAL	FORCE	RECRUITS
BATTLE	GENERAL	RIFLE
BAZOOKA	GUARD	ROCKETS
BOLD	HELMET	SALUTES
BRIGADE	INFANTRY	SPEARS
CAMP	LEGION	STAFF
CAVALRY	MAJOR	TANK
CONVOY	MARTIAL	TEAM
COUP	MILITARY	TRAIN
DIVISIONS	MISSILE	TROOPS
DRAFT	OFFICERS	UNITS

38

```
L I N C O L N H T U O M Y L P
D I S O W D R O F D A R B D L
L T V F C O H I L P T B A N O
E M U E A S L S E N T O T O T
E K L N R E T S E C R O W M S
D Y O E L P G V N B Z T O H I
S R D T I C O O Q U S L R C R
D L O S S C T O R J O E T I B
A N I F L A E E L R V H H R C
E N E S E L D S A N D W I C H
H T D N K R E H T B K G N A W
E X U O U E E W G E H L G I O
N N M T V W A H E T R N G H D
I K H I F E D R O F T A R T S
M A H R U D R N D G N I K O W
```

TWIN TOWN

60 sets of letters to be joined to form 30 English towns.
Then find them in the puzzle. One is done as an example.

DUR	LINC	NTRY	LEIC	~~WI~~
RPOOL	ORD	TFORD	STER	HEREF
OKE	NES	MINE	BRIG	BRAD
TLE	LIVE	ANDO	RED	THING
ING	FORD	ST	VER	OUTH
ATON	SAND	LE	LISK	ESTER
CARL	RUTH	ISLE	STOL	MOND
LLS	BRI	WE	~~GAN~~	COVE
SLOW	EDS	NUNE	HOUN	WORCE
RICH	HTON	RSHOT	WICH	HEAD
ALDE	WOK	TOT	BOO	HAM
WOR	PLYM	EARD	OLN	STRA

39

```
F E R E N O H P E L E T S K T
K G L D N S L O G E L E O E P
R C O Z K A F A D F S O D O S
E L I C Z C M N D R B D O T E
L I I T A U A N O D Y H W F T
R R S R S S P H O B E I G E A
B A D E E O G W E I S R L Y K
S S T K L N G A A T T B S L S
V T A T I B R O E S B C L O R
M N I K L C R R P A G U A P E
S U C L L E J A R V D I M O L
Y O R U T A G C M O Q U J N L
R O E D C S S Y L A L U H O O
W D Y K T E S S S E H C B M R
O P S O V R L L A B T O O F G
```

KIDDIES CORNER

The words in the following grid are all old favourites with children.

ACTION MAN

BOOK

BRICKS

CARDS

CHESS SET

CLUEDO

DOLL

DRUM

FOOTBALL

HULA/HOOP

JACKS

JIGSAW PUZZLE

LEGO

LUDO

MARBLES

MONOPOLY

POGO STICK

RATTLE

ROCKING
  HORSE

ROLLER
  SKATES

SCRABBLE

SNAKES AND/
  LADDERS

STILTS

TEDDY BEAR

TELEPHONE

TWISTER

YOYO

40

```
A S K P S H B E U G O L O R P
Y D O P R E L A C I R C L E Z
Y R O T R E P E R O U C S H C
A R B S T L M E S N R U T C A
P S T A L L S I P L O T R U T
S B P L A S R A E H E R E R I
C E M B E S Y J F R E A A T N
E S O N F C A O R M E P D A T
N U R E R E T D L U T F I I E
E O P P A N T O M I M E N N R
R H I E O A L D B W N I G C V
Y L R R E R O C N E K E S A A
S L F W D I R E C T O R S L L
O U R T H O D E E G A T S L R
B F Y C Y D E M O C K C A L B
```

THEATRE TIME

BIT PART

BLACK COME-
  DY

CIRCLE

CURTAIN CALL

DIRECTOR

ENCORE

FRONT OF
  HOUSE

FULL HOUSE

INTERVAL

LINES

PANTOMIME

PLOT

PREMIERE

PROLOGUE

PROMPT BOOK

PROPS

READINGS

REHEARSAL

REPERTORY

SCENARIO

SCENERY

STAGE

STALLS

TURNS

41

```
S T A R E N Y R U C R E M
A A D A M O V E L J K O E
T G T I S V E R S E O T T
E A E U R A N U S N C U E
L L N O R T U E V A L L O
L A A R X N S I P E D P R
I X L I D I O R E T S A C
T Y P E J U M M K H U V O
E V E L I N S I T E K N M
F J I O P R W R A Z Z L E
F R A G L E A Q A Q U A T
J U P I T E R E I M I C E
C O N S T E L L A T I O N
```

SPACED OUT

ASTEROID

COMET

CONSTEL-
   LATION

EARTH

GALAXY

JUPITER

MARS

MERCURY

METEOR

MOON

NEPTUNE

NOVA

PLANET

PLUTO

SATELLITE

SATURN

STAR

SUN

URANUS

VENUS

42

```
M I C H E L A N G E L O G
P O L L O C K U D E M A S
S H G O G N A V A Q U W E
R B K O S E C H A G A L L
E E Y C T S P E U L M T G
E A M T Y A A I R O I E R
M S A B R D N C D T R N E
R W S K R I N R I E U N C
E E U I S A A A M P B A O
V C N S T N N O V I E Z L
Z G U O O A G D M O N E T
M O V E I Y M L T W S C P
P I L A D R O D A V L A S
```

ART ATTACK

CEZANNE

CHAGALL

EL GRECO

GAUGUIN

GOYA

LAUTREC

LEONARDO

MATISSE

MICHELANGELO

MONET

PICASSO

POLLOCK

POUSSIN

RAPHAEL

REMBRANDT

RENOIR

RUBENS

SALVADOR DALI

TITIAN

VAN DYCK

VAN GOGH

VERMEER

WATTEAU

43

```
A S D H O K C I H C B A D
D K R V E M R K Q U I R D
B U Z Z A R D A L U A E R
W A C R T H O L L K A B A
P O T K S J F N E Y I I L
G I L U L I N N E T K K L
N H R L N I B W T P C S A
B H C C A C N E E O I U M
T A H I Y W R G C L D N E
N W N G R N S R O O R N S
R E N T C T O H V O A U F
E E H M A W S E A R S H C
T N A R O M R O C G N E L
```

BIRD SPOT

AVOCET	DABCHICK	QUAIL
BANTAM	DOVE	SHAG
BITTERN	DRAKE	SKUA
BULLFINCH	DUCKLING	SKYLARK
BUZZARD	GOOSE	SNIPE
COCK	HEN	SWALLOW
CORMORANT	HERON	TERN
CRANE	LINNET	THRUSH
CROW	MALLARD	
CURLEW	MARTIN	
CYGNET	OSTRICH	

44

```
E H B D N N O I N O M K P H R
L K C O L O S M K O T A E E L
B R N N R I T W O C R A C E S
A E E I E S A R E S I H M C L
T P E D K R H T N E I H O O R
E G O F W S F I X C T T T E T
G A M T U O P P K O C C G N T
E Z B M A A H E E H O N O O S
V P I K N G N C L N I H N R E
N A S D R A E O S G A O C T N
E C Q R N L B O B J W E H S R
L H U D E S M B I R D S P E M
L O E R T M O T A T O P D N A
U T Y E E M A H D N A T Y I L
C T R S U G A R A P S A H M C
```

SOUPER DOUPER

The words in the following grid are types of soup.

ASPARAGUS

BEEF/CONSOMME

BIRD'S/NEST

BORSH

CELERY

CHICKEN AND/
  SWEETCORN

CLAM/

CHOWDER

CULLEN/SKINK

FRENCH/ONION

GAZPACHO

LEEK/AND POTATO

LOBSTER/BISQUE

MINESTRONE

MUSHROOM

OXTAIL

PARSNIP AND/GINGER

PEA/AND HAM

POTAGE

SCOTCH/BROTH

THICK/VEGETABLE

TOMATO

WON/TON

45

```
F A T P N B A F F L E D D M C
Y D E S U M E B R Y K I E A F
P U S T D D O W Z Y T A K T L
D D P U E E E Z I H Z M C A U
I E U C L P I X E L I A O L S
S S D K Z D E R I F D Z H O T
C U B N Z D Y R R M B E S S E
O F D L U Q E U P O V D R S R
N N E E P O S L T L W A T E E
C O I G F T F H B E E U G L D
E C M M R E E N T U M X O U D
R S Y A U R A S O P O S E J E
T V T W E Z A T E C T R T D X
E E S D H N Z D E N N U T S O
D E I F I T S Y M D E L O I F
```

IN A STEW

AMAZED	DIZZY	PERPLEXED
AT A LOSS	FLUSTERED	PUZZLED
BAFFLED	FOILED	SHOCKED
BEMUSED	FOXED	STUCK
BEWILDERED	FRUSTRATED	STUMPED
BOTHERED	HAZY	STUNNED
CONFOUNDED	IN A STEW	STYMIED
CONFUSED	LOST	TROUBLED
DEFEATED	MIXED UP	UPSET
DISCONCERTED	MUZZY	VAGUE
DITHERY	MYSTIFIED	WORRIED

46

```
P K L A S T H O R E P L Y
E E A S S T C R U L E E D
T T T Y U R A L E L L E L
A A N U F R E Y L V U T O
R R A E E A R D I L A R C
R O R L S A P N O T E H S
A L A S V S F G T L A S K
N T E E R O I L A T P L O
E R R R R S E D T O R X T
T A R M E L L E U A B A E
B L L E E L R T L L L A W
P A T S E T O R P K L E G
B L L T T L E R R A U Q U
```

TALK, TALK

ASSERT	PREACH	TELL
AVER	PROTEST	YAK
CHATTER	QUARREL	YELP
DISSENT	RANT	
EULOGISE	RAVE	
EXPLODE	RELATE	
FUSS	REPLY	
GAB	SCOLD	
INFORM	SPOUT	
NARRATE	TALK	
ORATE	TATTLE	

47

```
E T I G H T S O M N M M T
X S T U D E N T S Z I M U
E J N N T A D B Z N R R R
R B B N I L C A N O R R N
C C S P M U J L O M O E S
I B A S P A E L A U R H E
S T O L I P F E B S F C M
E B B Y L R R T N I S A U
S M O V E M E N T C O E T
B M H T Y H R A B L L T S
N B C L L I P V O V F G O
N E W S T E P S B B J N C
N B B O S N S D R O C E R
```

STEP TO IT

BALLET

CLASSES

COSTUMES

EXERCISES

FLOOR

JAZZ

JUMPS

LEAPS

MIRROR

MOVEMENT

MUSIC

NEW STEPS

PIANO

RECORDS

RHYTHM

SOLO

STUDENTS

TAP

TAPES

TEACHER

TIGHTS

TURNS

48

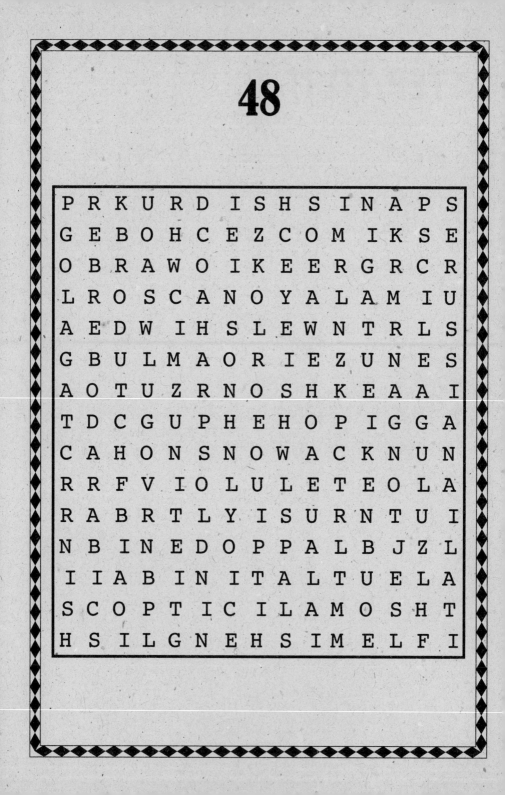

```
P R K U R D I S H S I N A P S
G E B O H C E Z C O M I K S E
O B R A W O I K E E R G R C R
L R O S C A N O Y A L A M I U
A E D W I H S L E W N T R L S
G B U L M A O R I E Z U N E S
A O T U Z R N O S H K E A A I
T D C G U P H E H O P I G G A
C A H O N S N O W A C K N U N
R R F V I O L U L E T E O L A
R A B R T L Y I S U R N T U I
N B I N E D O P P A L B J Z L
I I A B I N I T A L T U E L A
S C O P T I C I L A M O S H T
H S I L G N E H S I M E L F I
```

CAN YOU SPEAK...

ALEUT	FRENCH	NEPALI
ARABIC	GAELIC	OSCAN
AZTEC	GREEK	PERSIAN
BERBER	HEBREW	RUSSIAN
BINI	HOPI	SOMALI
CANTONESE	IRISH	SPANISH
COPTIC	ITALIAN	TAGALOG
CZECH	KIOWA	TONGAN
DUTCH	KURDISH	VOGUL
EDO	LAPP	WELSH
ENGLISH	LATIN	ZULU
ESKIMO	MALAY	ZUNI
FLEMISH	MAORI	

49

```
D G J L P E N I B R U T U A Q
S T A P L E R C Z T L E Y B E
A R E T U P M O C F R L T F T
O E D I V S E N G I N E I R U
S H J D C M C V X L E P I T O
D S F U X O B E K U J H O A A
F A M G N W V Y B N R O T O M
N W W O V E B O C M Q N S S E
G H R N O R N R V P W E D S H
J S I E X L A T U R B O J E T
V I N R C N M L R E X I M R A
M D G I E B L H C S H G F P L
G H E S Y I K J Z S H O I S T
K B R Z M M R O T A V E L E D
S X O M A N Y D S F J L K J G
```

MACHINE MAYHEM

COMPUTER   JUKE-BOX   TELEPHONE

CONVEYOR   LATHE   TILL

CRANE   LIFT   TURBINE

DISHWASHER   LOOM   TURBO-JET

DRIER   MILL   VIDEO

DYNAMO   MIXER   WRINGER

ELEVATOR   MOTOR

ENGINE   MOWER

ESPRESSO   PRESS

FAN   SIREN

HOIST   STAPLER

50

```
E L T E E B A A D A C I C H A
S H B Y S P I D E R D E L T A
Z O S U H C H M R O W D O O W
B O T I U Q S O M S B E E M Y
U C D A T E G D I M S P T L L
T E J T A N G L E A N I E F F
T A N A M T A O B R E T A W Y
E L O C U S T M R M I N A E A
R R P C Y A P P G M K E H N M
F O S R C E S Y R N C C P R T
L U H I C A T E R P I L L A R
Y C F C W R T S W I T Y R K S
W O L K R W D R I B Y D A L T
H W E E V I L D E R B Y S R W
Y K A T T G Y T E N R O H S P
```

INSECT WORLD

ANT	FLEA	TERMITE
APHID	GNAT	TICK
BEE	HORNET	WASP
BEETLE	LADYBIRD	WATER BOATMAN
BUTTERFLY	LOCUST	WEEVIL
CATERPILLAR	MAYFLY	WOODWORM
CENTIPEDE	MIDGE	
CHRYSALIS	MOSQUITO	
CICADA	MOTH	
CRICKET	PRAYING MANTIS	
EARWIG	SPIDER	

51

```
E O V E R T I M E V E C N
M D N S E C O N D I A L N
I A R S M I D D A Y H O E
T Y N O O N R E T F A C B
T U T H G I N N S L K G
S R N O O N R W U N F W I
O E R U T U F N A N H O B
P A G N I N R O M D O R E
N T W I L I G H T F U K D
T N P A S T E T A D R E T
T I M E S H E E T N N E I
Q M I N U T E H A N D W M
N E N O Y A D A Y T I M E
```

TIMELY

AFTERNOON

BEDTIME

BIG BEN

CLOCKWORK

DAWN

DAY ONE

DAYTIME

DIAL

FUTURE

HALF HOUR

HOUR HAND

MAN-HOUR

MIDDAY

MINUTE HAND

MORNING

NIGHT

NOON

OVERTIME

PAST

POST TIME

SECOND

SUNRISE

SUNSET

TIME SHEET

TWILIGHT

WEEK

52

```
Z U C A R N A T I O N U V
M I H D U K A P U R C H L
D Y G M P A I L O N G A M
L S P A K T N I E S U X Y
O Y U P R M U E S R Y L D
G V N C O D T N E Z I P A
I U M O S P E L S L U A F
R H C P E I P N Q I I D F
A I F D T P B P I L U T O
M S R A W J A I H A M H D
U H P I Q N C A H C P O I
C M R S S U D R C U L D L
I Y D Y A E P T E E W S Z
```

BLOOMERS

CARNATION

DAFFODIL

DAHLIA

DAISY

GARDENIA

HIBISCUS

IMPATIENS

IRIS

LAUREL

LILAC

LILY

MAGNOLIA

MARIGOLD

PANSY

PEONY

PETUNIA

POPPY

POSY

ROSE

SWEET PEA

TULIP

53

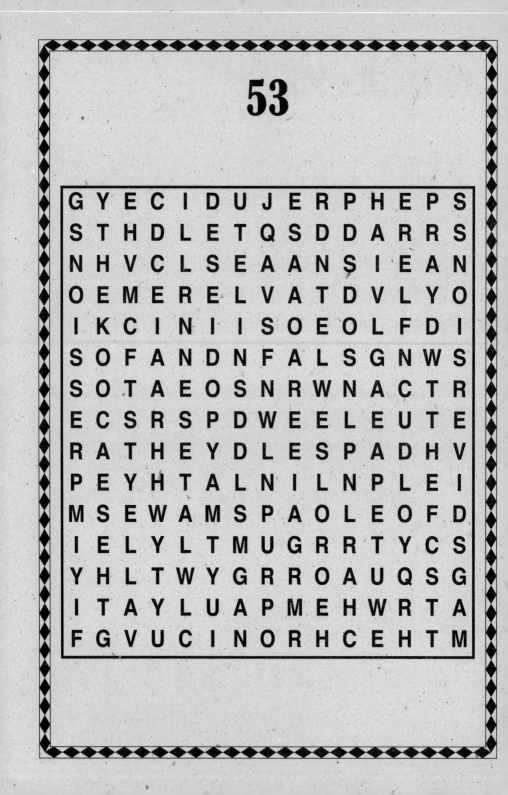

```
G Y E C I D U J E R P H E P S
S T H D L E T Q S D D A R R S
N H V C L S E A A N Ş I E A N
O E M E R E L V A T D V L Y O
I K C I N I I S O E O L F D I
S O F A N D N F A L S G N W S
S O T A E O S N R W N A C T R
E C S R S P D W E E L E U T E
R A T H E Y D L E S P A D H V
P E Y H T A L N I L N P L E I
M S E W A M S P A O L E O F D
I E L Y L T M U G R R T Y C S
Y H L T W Y G R R O A U Q S G
I T A Y L U A P M E H W R T A
F G V U C I N O R H C E H T M
```

CHANGE THE NAME

The words in the following grid are the original names of some famous books and the names by which they are now known. Can you match the pairs? There is one extra title. By what name is this book better known?

ALL'S WELL/THAT/
   ENDS WELL

DAVID/COPPERFIELD

EAST OF/EDEN

FIRST/IMPRESSIONS

MAG'S DIVERSIONS

PAUL/MOREL

PRIDE AND/PREJUDICE

SALINAS/VALLEY

SONS AND/LOVERS

THE CHRONIC/
   ARGONAUTS

THE SEA-COOK

TREASURE/ISLAND

WAR AND PEACE

```
P A S T E L P A M U D L A C P
C O R N S Y D N A C T S R F E
F O B E E E G A D N A B R U A
H C T N P V V P D S P E Q D N
C M O T P A E R P O K N H G U
T H O M O C P O E C U E Q E T
O D A L A N P Y I S S G P D N
C T M N A I T T L I E O H A E
S A P A L S S O V F X R V L M
R I R L E R S E F Y F E P A E
E E O A E R G E D F L S L M C
T L P P M L C C S C E I A R K
T A M A U E B E R L A N E A M
U U R E T A L O C O H C S M A
B U B B L E G U M I Y L L E J
```

STICK TO IT

ADHESIVE

BANDAGE

BUBBLE GUM

BUMPER
  STICKER

BUTTERSCOTCH

CANDY

CARAMEL

CEMENT

CHOCOLATE

CORN

COTTON

DOUGH

EPOXY

FLYPAPER

FUDGE

GLUE

HONEY

ICE CREAM

JAM

JELLY

LAC

LOLLIPOPS

MAPLE

MARMALADE

MOLASSES

MUD

PASTE

PEANUT

PECAN PIE

PRESERVES

RESIN

SAP

SEAL

STAMP

TAPE

TAR

VELCRO

55

```
A W R N O I S I V E L E T L E
D P E L O R C L T T M S A R E
D F P P A U E S I U S S T C K
G R A L R U C U I N R A N E T
S R E T A R D R C A E E C C N
T T A S I U O I E H I S V N I
S I A P S T S H T D W H Y A A
N T T G I E E E U I S O S M P
E P C D E R R A M P O H B R E
M E U A Y D E M O C O N E O S
U A P A R T V R S W X T V F A
T H L A N M P S M L I F I R E
S P M E T V A M E N I C L E R
O A G H G U O R H T N U R P G
C A S M O O R G N I S S E R D
```

ACTING UP

The words in the following grid are all associated with acting.

ACT	CUE	PLAY
AGENT	CURTAIN	PROPS
APPLAUSE	DRAMA	REHEARSAL
AUDIENCE	DRESSER	ROLE
AUDITION	DRESSING ROOM	RUN THROUGH
AUDITORIUM	FILMS	SCRIPT
BOW	GREASEPAINT	SHOW
CAST	LINES	STAGE
CINEMA	LIVE	TAPE
COMEDY	PART	TELEVISION
COSTUME	PERFORMANCE	THEATRE

56

```
W T C S P E E D Q T S U D
S M P D L X L L L R I P R
L I C R B V O M P A G F L
R E D L U O H S S P N H C
D V K E Y T H P F P D E Y
E V P M I F H R M D S R C
S T O N E A M A J U R F I
O T S C L K R O W F B N F
L W R T D T D P G K R O F
C W O R R A N B J T R P A
P S A S L E F T R U C K R
K C D B X C E R N G J S T
F D Z F R U O T E D F S J
```

STREET WISE

ASPHALT	SHOULDER
BUMP	SIDE
CLOSED	SIGN
DETOUR	SPEED
DUST	STONE
FORK	STREET
HOLE	TRAFFIC
LANE	TRUCK
NARROW	WORK
RAMP	YIELD
ROAD	

57

```
Z O I B Y P P A N S W Q E
U F H V D A T E C H U T N
O C L I Y Y O O C I S A N
S D P E D U O W C A T T E
P A T A E T O K H B R P D
R A R Q E T E S P U R T D
I T W L P M A A Z E R N U
N B F M S L C I S O M R S
T Y O I F E P T D A S H Y
K R Q A W O O E N E D U D
P H S U R S F E T H M W A
M T B E O T N O R P R M T
W O J H U S T L E L C S I
```

ZIPPY!

DART

DASH

DEFT

FAST

FLASH

FLEET

HASTE

HURRY

HUSTLE

IMMEDIATE

PRESTO

PROMPT

PRONTO

QUICK

RACE

RAPID

RUSH

SCOOT

SNAPPY

SPEEDY

SPRINT

SPURT

SUDDEN

SWIFT

ZIP

58

```
T C M A S W C H U G I T P I N
I O R I N I T S L S N A I D S
F V E E R N O W P U L L G I T
E R T S I W H I C T A F E N A
C U I T R I C T I I O N U R L
R I C E P P C O R E L R T E M
H T G R O L R D T C E A L T E
G I N S C O U E V E R E R T A
I R E M Y C I S I R D F R O R
L W T E T I R C R E W R I G E
G I R R N S T C C O S U T T E
U R E O I E L E K E T O L E A
L I K U P U C R A E E R L A R
P N A N D I C I F C P M I N T
A G E R B T E S U A L R E T H
```

POWER IT

Starting at the letter (S) move up, down, left or right to find the electrical words listed below. The last item (not listed) is an electrical appliance.

Electrical appliance: _____

CIRCUIT BREAKER

COLOUR CODE

EARTH TERMINAL

ELECTRICITY METER

ELECTRIC PLUG

DIGITAL METER

FLAT PINS

INSULATION

LIGHTING CIRCUIT

MAIN SWITCH

NEUTRAL

REFIT COVER

REPLACE A FUSE

ROUND PINS

SCREWDRIVER

SOCKET OUTLET

SWITCH ON

WIRE STRIPPERS

WIRING A PLUG

59

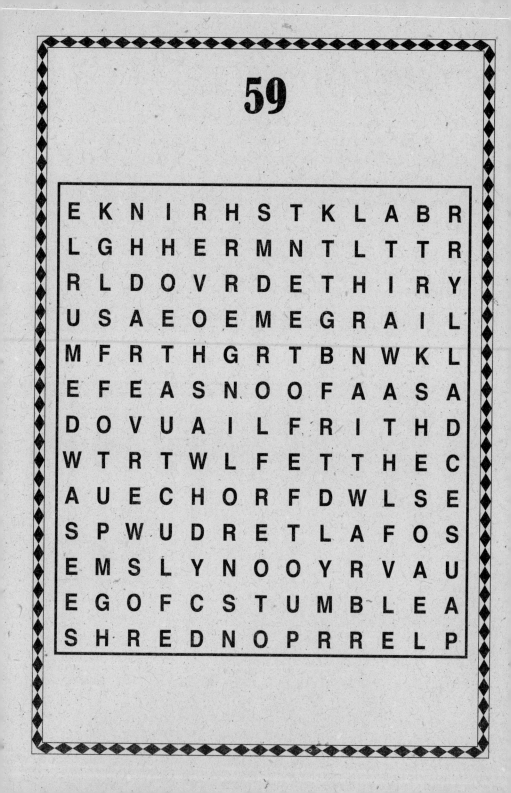

```
E K N I R H S T K L A B R
L G H H E R M N T L T T R
R L D O V R D E T H I R Y
U S A E O E M E G R A I L
M F R T H G R T B N W K L
E F E A S N O O F A A S A
D O V U A I L F R I T H D
W T R T W L F E T T H E C
A U E C H O R F D W L S E
S P W U D R E T L A F O S
E M S L Y N O O Y R V A U
E G O F C S T U M B L E A
S H R E D N O P R R E L P
```

TAKE YOUR TIME

ALTERNATE	HEDGE	STALL
BALK	HOLD OFF	STUMBLE
CHANGE	HOVER	SWERVE
DALLY	LINGER	WAIT
DEBATE	PAUSE	
DELAY	PONDER	
DEMUR	PUT OFF	
EVADE	SEESAW	
FALTER	SHIFT	
FENCE	SHRINK	
FLUCTUATE	SKIRT	

60

```
M Q N L E T T E R S M L P
E R U G I F J R L K P H R
K L O Q I C H A A A L E A
R X B F X S I T T C P C C
Z P V B A T E T C A E H T
I E R N I B E D P N A S I
T N S N A R S G G I M C C
I C I H N P C T N G A R E
F I P S A L K S R R R A T
F L C G I P V I T A K W I
A L I N K S E O N M C L R
R S E L D O O D C S M T W
G S V R T N I O P L L A B
```

PAPER PLAY

ABSTRACT

ALPHABET

BALLPOINT

CARTOON

CHAIN

DESIGN

DOODLES

FIGURE

FORM

GRAFFITI

INITIALS

LETTERS

LINES

LINKS

MARGIN

MARK

NAPKINS

PAPER

PATTERNS

PENCIL

PRACTICE

SCRAWL

SCRIBBLE

SHAPE

TRACE

WRITE

61

```
R E N R A G F A N R U B O C E
E Y I F A O K A R S M E N R L
B W O M L N H X B N H A E C E
R X O L A G A R F I E L D T I
U L E O A L I T L D T S K A T
H T J L D A O T T S R L S Y H
T L L E W S O B I A A O G L G
S A F R E N T H P D W A A O U
C Z G K T R W E K F E N L R A
O A R C A M E R O N T D W H N
R U G U A C N R O M S W A M T
B Q T N U A K I C M A Y Y N L
E S G R E I N O I O T S U C A
T A B U N Y H T V E B H O N S
T H O G R U H T R A C A M N T
```

JAMES WHO?

ARNESS	DEAN	LAST
BOLAM	FOLLETT	MACARTHUR
BOSWELL	FOX	MASON
BRUCE	GALWAY	NAUGHTIE
BURKE	GARFIELD	SLOAN
CAAN	GARNER	STEWART
CAGNEY	GOLDSMITH	STUART
CALLAGHAN	HAYTER	TAYLOR
CAMERON	HERRIOTT	THURBER
COBURN	HILTON	WATTANA
COOK	HUNT	WHISTLER
CORBETT	KING	WOODS

62

```
B C E R L Y R E D I O R B M E
J O G N I T T I F A D E C A L
Y P B D I A R B S L E M W S B
T A H B Z H I X K C U R N I M
T T G N I K C O M S A O H A I
A T B S P N Z A N G T L T T H
P E T A C K S Q M T N E L O T
E R E K C I P N U G R I O O S
M N E M C I S B G I N K C T P
E G S S C A O S A N A I I A E
A G N O S V R L O N I T W M F
S M T I P S A K D R C N I E D
U P E I G C T E C H S R I F S
R G N H A D Y U C I T S A L E
E S E L D E E N D F R I L L B
```

SEW ON

BOBBINS

BRAID

BUTTONS

EDGING

ELASTIC

EMBROIDERY

FACING

FITTING

FRILL

HEM

HOOK AND EYE

LACE

LINING

MATERIAL

NEEDLES

PATTERN

PICOT

PINS

PRESS-STUD

RICKRACK

SCALLOP

SCISSORS

SEWING-MACHINE

SMOCKING

STITCH

TACK

TAPE MEA-
SURE

THIMBLE

THREAD

TRIM

UNPICKER

ZIP

63

```
R E W O P C A E S C A P E T B
E D H M C L E L L A B N M I O
T X A B A P J O I N I A F R L
H D T R M D R A U G K W O O D
G O M I P F G I N S H G R N S
I S W G N R O E E L U T N S C
F I K A Z G I O E N N P U O Y
P D N D E M U Q R O E T A R G
A E L E C T R I C P J L E R L
B Q U G A H A X S G Z L V E T
R U A D L I W R O H L L I R D
I S C E P X T L M I E K D B N
C B S K R O W N T S E R O F A
K O Y W E R G R A C T M O V R
H Y N O I T A T S M B D R F B
```

FIRED UP

The words in the following list can be preceded or followed by the word 'fire'.

ALARM	DRILL	LOG
ARMS	ELECTRIC	MAN
ARTILLERY	ENGINE	PLACE
BALL	ESCAPE	POWER
BOMB	EXTINGUISHER	PROOF
BRAND	FIGHTER	SCREEN
BRICK	FOREST	SIDE
BRIGADE	GAS	STATION
BUCKET	GRATE	TRAP
CAMP	GUARD	WILD
COAL	GUN	WOOD
CONTROL	HOSE	WORKS
DAMP	IRONS	
DOOR	LIGHT	

64

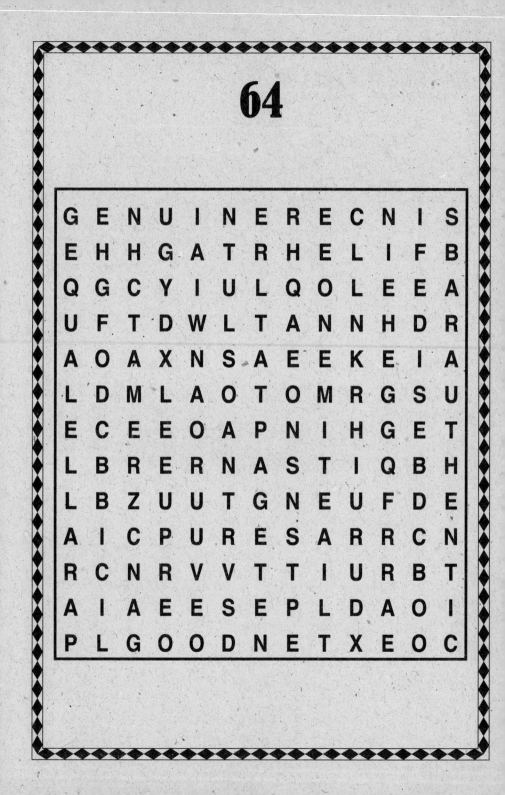

```
G E N U I N E R E C N I S
E H H G A T R H E L I F B
Q G C Y I U L Q O L E E A
U F T D W L T A N N H D R
A O A X N S A E E K E I A
L D M L A O T O M R G S U
E C E E O A P N I H G E T
L B R E R N A S T I Q B H
L B Z U U T G N E U F D E
A I C P U R E S A R R C N
R C N R V V T T I U R B T
A I A E E S E P L D A O I
P L G O O D N E T X E O C
```

BE HONEST

ABREAST	EVEN	RIGHT
ACCURATE	FILE	RULE
ALIGN	GENUINE	SINCERE
ALONGSIDE	GOOD	TRUE
AUTHENTIC	HONEST	
BAR	LINE	
BESIDE	MATCH	
COEXTEND	NATURAL	
CORRESPOND	PARALLEL	
EQUAL	PURE	
EQUATE	REAL	

65

```
O A I S R A E P P A S I D
Y A W A T R A T S T I X E
I E E T A C A V W R I X N
O E F F O H S U P I O W T
I F F O E B I E M D W Y R
T F W R I E U A U W R A A
U O I E E I L S W R D W I
O E K W M S T I E A I A N
R K W L B R E I O T W O E
A A I E A I N R I E O G U
E T I P R W O E I W R U S
L V E A K S G H R D J R T
C D E C A M P E V A E L Q
```

STARTING OUT

AWAY	GONE
BE OFF	LEAVE
CLEAR OUT	PUSH OFF
DECAMP	RIDE
DEPART	ROAD
DISAPPEAR	SET OUT
EMBARK	START
ENTRAIN	TAKE OFF
EXIT	VACATE
EXODUS	WALK
GO AWAY	

66

```
N H N H N S I V A M R R P R B
C Y T V E B E R Y L N C O A N
H A E I L A E R I C A R P Y D
E C L O R N T N E N O Y P G A
R I O L A L N H B S L S Y E W
R N I A E R O S E N Y T D N N
Y T V N P Z B M O R R A A E I
N H L N N R A N H N I L P M V
O L I V E R N H P S N Y H E Y
Y P S H Y L I L Y R I B N R P
E J A S M I N E D U B U E Y A
O N B L A U R E L S O R P I N
J A S P E R N N I T R A M R S
Y L L O M A R I G O L D I I Y
A U R O R A N P R I M R O S E
```

NATURE'S WAY

All these names have connections with nature.

AURORA	GENE	LILY	POPPY
BASIL	HAZEL	MARIGOLD	PRIMROSE
BERYL	HEATHER	MARTIN	RAY
BUD	HERB	MAVIS	ROBIN
CHERRY	HYACINTH	MOLLY	ROSE
CRYSTAL	IRIS	MYRTLE	ROSEMARY
DAISY	IVY	OLIVE	RUBY
DAPHNE	JASMINE	OPAL	VIOLA
DAWN	JASPER	PANSY	VIOLET
EMERY	JOEY	PEARL	
ERICA	LAUREL	PHOEBE	

67

```
F A C T O R G D N E U N I M D
G E D I V I S O R P Q U E U D
G E O M E T R Y A R B E G L A
A D D E N D I I N F I N I T Y
S I N S A E L G N A I R T I R
C F E U R P O I E R E W O P T
I F D U I C I R C L E R T L E
T E I T T H A S A E I S H Y M
A R V R H I S U N I T O A I O
M E I A M W Q L I O P D U B N
E N D E E E U P S U N I M W O
H C I E T W A W E L O G I C G
T E S N I O R E D I V I D O I
A U I D C Y E L G N A T C E R
M O D U L U S U B T R A C T T
```

YOUR NUMBER'S UP

ADD	EQUAL	RECTANGLE
ADDEND	FACTOR	SET
ALGEBRA	GEOMETRY	SQUARE
ARITHMETIC	INFINITY	SUBTRACT
BASE	LOGIC	SUM
CIRCLE	MATHEMATICS	TIMES
DIFFERENCE	MINUS	TRIANGLE
DIGIT	MODULUS	TRIGONOMETRY
DIVIDE	MULTIPLY	UNIT
DIVIDEND	PLUS	
DIVISOR	POWER	

68

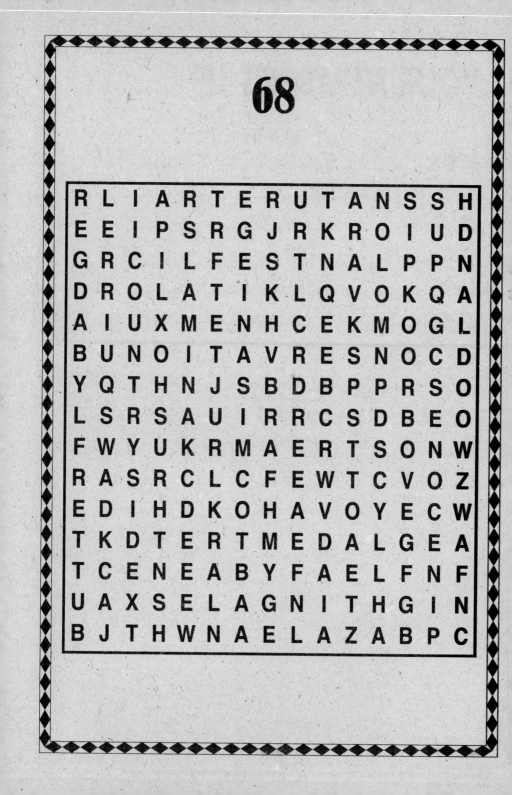

```
R L I A R T E R U T A N S S H
E E I P S R G J R K R O I U D
G R C I L F E S T N A L P P N
D R O L A T I K L Q V O K Q A
A I U X M E N H C E K M O G L
B U N O I T A V R E S N O C D
Y Q T H N J S B D B P P R S O
L S R S A U I R R C S D B E O
F W Y U K R M A E R T S O N W
R A S R C L C F E W T C V O Z
E D I H D K O H A V O Y E C W
T K D T E R T M E D A L G E A
T C E N E A B Y F A E L F N F
U A X S E L A G N I T H G I N
B J T H W N A E L A Z A B P C
```

NATURE TRAIL

ANIMALS

AZALEA

BADGER

BRACKEN

BROOK

BUTTERFLY

CONSERVA-
   TION

COUNTRYSIDE

FLOWERS

FOREST

GLADE

HEATHER

JACKDAW

LEAFY

NATURE TRAIL

NIGHTINGALE

OAK

OXLIP

PINE CONES

PLANTS

SILVER BIRCH

SQUIRREL

STREAM

THRUSH

WOODLAND

WOODPECKER

69

```
I  V  R  B  N  A  N  S  O  R  S  U
P  S  E  K  A  C  T  M  D  F  N  A
R  N  T  L  O  R  I  H  K  T  R  P
I  A  H  I  G  S  O  R  I  O  S  G
O  I  S  T  P  I  T  L  U  M  N  E
S  E  G  A  N  G  A  O  E  L  I  R
O  A  N  E  I  S  N  G  R  N  C  S
I  S  T  U  T  R  T  R  E  A  V  A
L  D  R  T  A  O  S  L  N  I  R  M
O  M  S  O  N  H  I  B  R  B  K  S
```

SQUARE UP

Find 3x3 squares in the diagram that contain, in no particular order, the nine letters of the words listed.

CARNATION

CARNIVALS

DUST STORM

GENERATOR

HISTORIAN

LIMOUSINE

PAINTINGS

RIVERBANK

SIGNATURE

SOFT DRINK

SPOTLIGHT

70

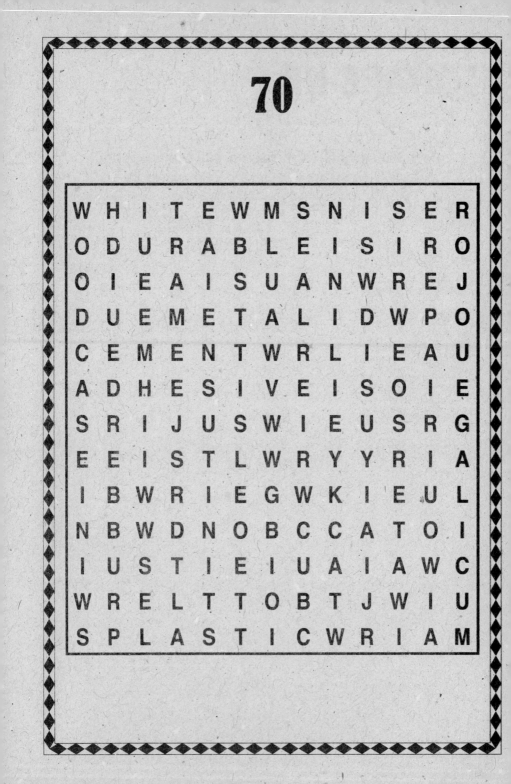

```
W H I T E W M S N I S E R
O D U R A B L E I S I R O
O I E A I S U A N W R E J
D U E M E T A L I D W P O
C E M E N T W R L I E A U
A D H E S I V E I S O I E
S R I J U S W I E U S R G
E E I S T L W R Y Y R I A
I B W R I E G W K I E U L
N B W D N O B C C A T O I
I U S T I E I U A I A W C
W R E L T T O B T J W I U
S P L A S T I C W R I A M
```

STUCK ON YOU

ADHESIVE	RUBBER
BOND	SEAL
BOTTLE	STICKY
CEMENT	TACKY
DURABLE	TUBE
GLUE	WATER
MEND	WELD
METAL	WHITE
MUCILAGE	WOOD
PLASTIC	
REPAIR	
RESIN	

71

```
H E N L Y S W E R D N A T S H
W I P O R W H I T E C I T Y E
O S G O O D I S O N P A R K E
L M E H T R T S E L M T R A G
D R O W B I T A N F L W Y H A
T D N S O U S X O R B I N C T
R O O L P C R R T S W C O T O
A O T E O E D Y S A E K D A O
F W N T E B R Y R H M E E H C
F D I S R R E N E R Y N L S N
O O M I D L T N V A L H B D E
R O D I S R L N L Y E A M N V
D G A I R E O N I R B M I A A
E R B A Y T I L S A I H W R C
L A V O T E K R A M W E N B C
```

SPORTS GROUNDS

AINTREE	IBROX
ASCOT	LORDS
AYR	NEWMARKET
BADMINTON	OLD TRAFFORD
BISLEY	OVAL
BRANDS HATCH	SILVERSTONE
COWES	STAMFORD BRIDGE
EPSOM	ST. ANDREWS
GOODISON PARK	TROON
GOODWOOD	TWICKENHAM
HENLEY	WHITE CITY
HIGHBURY	WIMBLEDON

72

```
C E I L I N G E M O N F E
B A S T U T E E H S O S T
E G T A B L E C L O T H O
D E N B C E R K R M A R S
S O U I L W H E N O P O N
P L M O H O O D C A I U I
R E B E I T R L R V L D A
E S R N O C O W L E D B T
A D E K S A M L A I O E R
D N L P K M A N C L P O U
N I L U A P R A T R I D C
I L A E T R I C A N O P Y
R B E N L I D C F T O L A
```

COVERED UP

BEDSPREAD
BLANKET
BLINDS
CANOPY
CARPET
CEILING
CLOAK
CLOTHING
COWL
CURTAINS
DOME
DRAPES
HOOD
LID
MASK

PALL
PILLOWCASE
ROOF
SHEET
SHROUD
TABLECLOTH
TARPAULIN
TOWEL
UMBRELLA
VEIL
WRAP

73

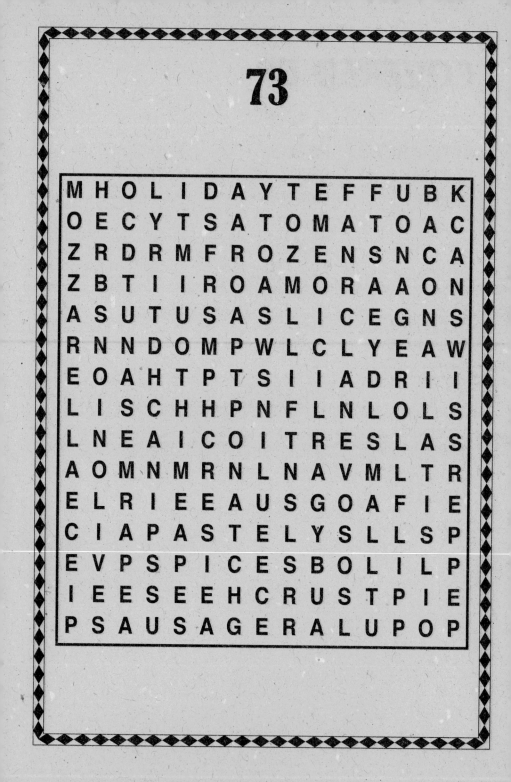

```
M H O L I D A Y T E F F U B K
O E C Y T S A T O M A T O A C
Z R D R M F R O Z E N S N C A
Z B T I I R O A M O R A A O N
A S U T U S A S L I C E G N S
R N N D O M P W L C L Y E A W
E O A H T P T S I I A D R I I
L I S C H H P N F L N L O L S
L N E A I C O I T R E S L A S
A O M N M R N L N A V M L T R
E L R I E E A U S G O A F I E
C I A P A S T E L Y S L L S P
E V P S P I C E S B O L I L P
I E E S E E H C R U S T P I E
P S A U S A G E R A L U P O P
```

PIZZA BASE

AROMA
BACON
BUFFET
CALL
CHEESE
CRISP
CRUST
FINE
FLIP
FLOUR
FROZEN
GARLIC
HERBS
HOLIDAY
ITALIAN
LUNCH

MEDIUM
MILD
MOZZARELLA
OILS
OLIVES
ONIONS
OREGANO
OVEN
PARMESAN
PASTE
PEPPERONI
PEPPERS
PIECE
POPULAR
ROLL
SALT

SAUSAGE
SLICE
SMALL
SNACK
SOFT
SPICES
SPINACH
SWISS
TASTY
THIN
TOMATO
TOPPINGS
TUNA
WARM
YEAST

```
T E T C E F E R P H E A D
R C O U R S E O M A X E K
A H J Q U H L T K R S R D
S A P O C P B I O L O G Y
C L H A I O R N P W L F B
I L E V E L A O E U Q S G
E T A C T K E M J E P N N
N O R S N I O V R E I A I
C M E C S H F U E T C G D
E T N H G R T M I L A T A
S K O O B C O R R M O L E
E M H O E T W O E E H G R
H S I L G N E S M A T H S
```

HIGHER LEARNING

A-LEVEL   HEAD   SCHOOL
ART   HOMEWORK   SCIENCE
BIOLOGY   HOUSE   TEACHER
BOOKS   LECTURE   TERM
CLASSROOM   MATHS   TEST
COURSE   MONITOR   WRITING
ENGLISH   O-LEVEL
EXAM   PREFECT
FORM   PROJECT
GAMES   PUPILS
HALL   READING

75

```
P P I N S E B G H P
A R I P L E A A R R
F B A T R N K O R K
S I T H S O J I E B
P E N P S E N E P A
N O I E C R N G C S
F N I T F N O U E E
Y A I N E I I Z G D
P O N S T T N D A O
N O S G Y S E K N R
```

SHARP END

ACUITY

BARB

EDGE

FANG

FINE

KEENNESS

KNIFE

NETTLE

NIBS

PINS

POINTS

PROJECTION

PRONGED

RAZOR-SHARP

SNAG

SPIKES

SPINY

SOLUTIONS

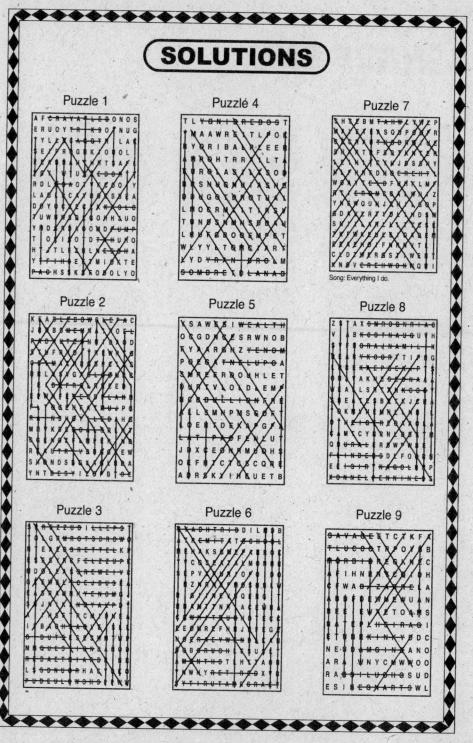

Puzzle 1

Puzzle 4

Puzzle 7

Song: Everything I do.

Puzzle 2

Puzzle 5

Puzzle 8

Puzzle 3

Puzzle 6

Puzzle 9

SOLUTIONS

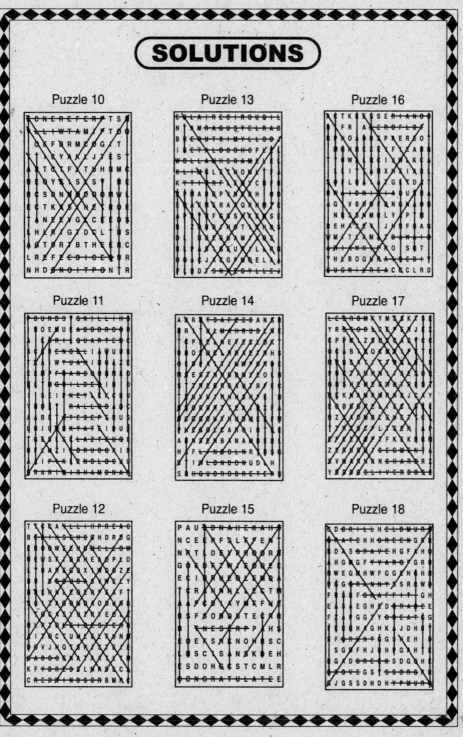

Puzzle 10

Puzzle 13

Puzzle 16

Puzzle 11

Puzzle 14

Puzzle 17

Puzzle 12

Puzzle 15

Puzzle 18

SOLUTIONS

Puzzle 19

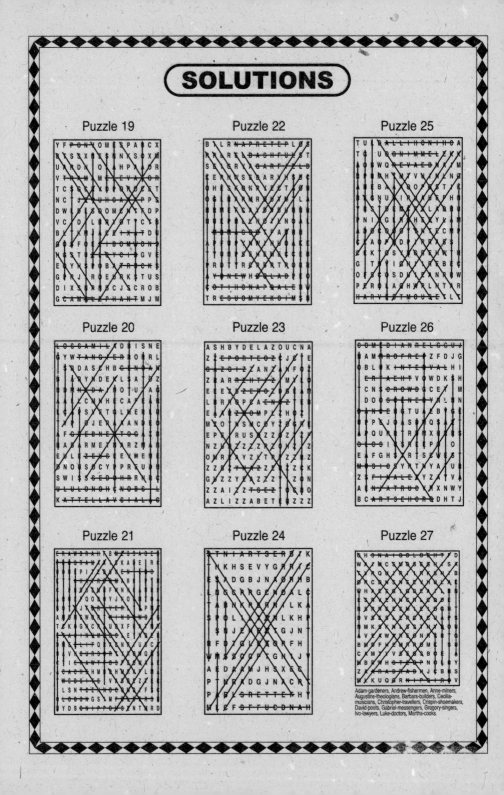

Puzzle 22

Puzzle 25

Puzzle 20

Puzzle 23

Puzzle 26

Puzzle 21

Puzzle 24

Puzzle 27

Adam-gardeners, Andrew-fishermen, Anne-miners,
Augustine-theologians, Barbara-builders, Cecilia-
musicians, Christopher-travellers, Crispin-shoemakers,
David-poets, Gabriel-messengers, Gregory-singers,
Ivo-lawyers, Luke-doctors, Martha-cooks.

SOLUTIONS

Puzzle 28

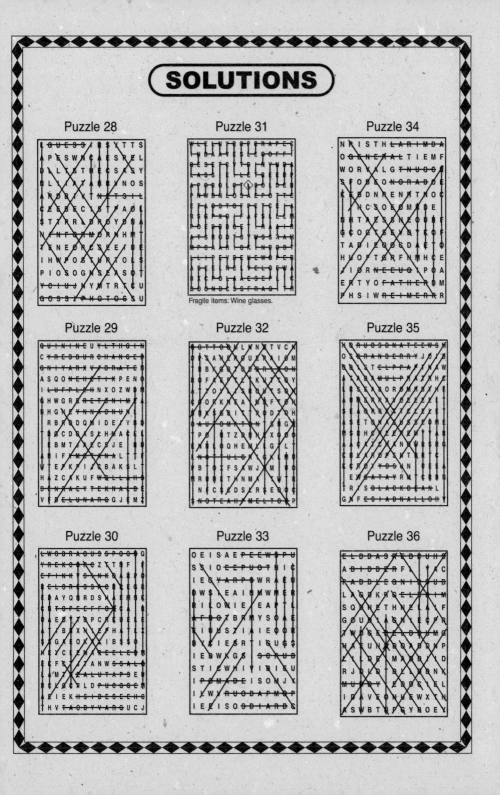

Puzzle 31

Fragile items: Wine glasses.

Puzzle 34

Puzzle 29

Puzzle 32

Puzzle 35

Puzzle 30

Puzzle 33

Puzzle 36

SOLUTIONS

Puzzle 37
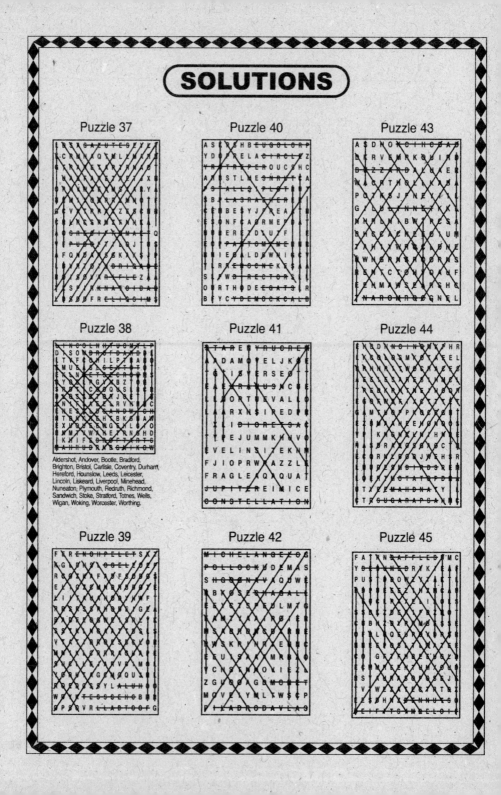

Puzzle 40

Puzzle 43

Puzzle 38

Aldershot, Andover, Bootle, Bradford, Brighton, Bristol, Carlisle, Coventry, Durham, Hereford, Hounslow, Leeds, Leicester, Lincoln, Liskeard, Liverpool, Minehead, Nuneaton, Plymouth, Redruth, Richmond, Sandwich, Stoke, Stratford, Totnes, Wells, Wigan, Woking, Worcester, Worthing.

Puzzle 41

Puzzle 44

Puzzle 39

Puzzle 42

Puzzle 45

SOLUTIONS

Puzzle 46

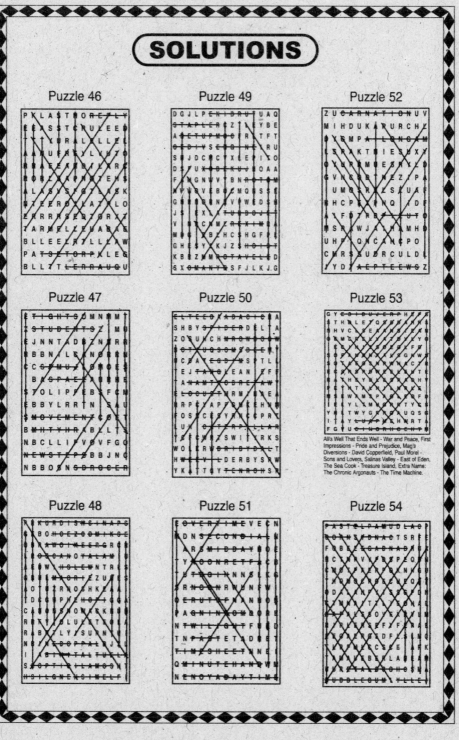

Puzzle 49

Puzzle 52

Puzzle 47

Puzzle 50

Puzzle 53

All's Well That Ends Well - War and Peace, First
Impressions - Pride and Prejudice, Mag's
Diversions - David Copperfield, Paul Morel -
Sons and Lovers, Salinas Valley - East of Eden,
The Sea Cook - Treasure Island, Extra Name:
The Chronic Argonauts - The Time Machine.

Puzzle 48

Puzzle 51

Puzzle 54

SOLUTIONS

Puzzle 55

Puzzle 58

Electrical appliance: Refrigerator.

Puzzle 61

Puzzle 56

Puzzle 59

Puzzle 62

Puzzle 57

Puzzle 60

Puzzle 63

SOLUTIONS

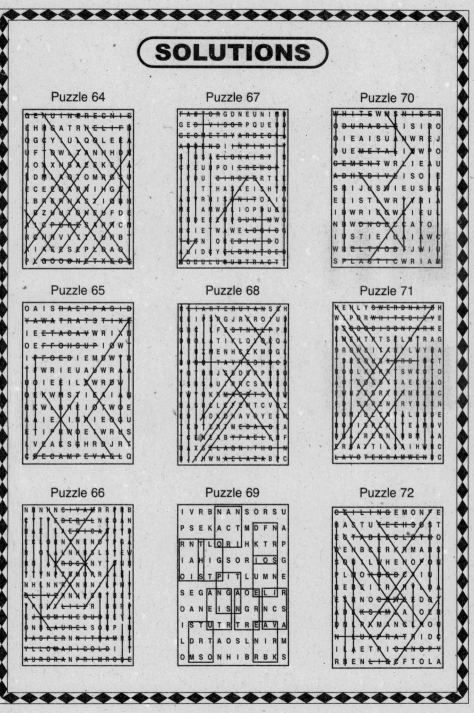

Puzzle 64
Puzzle 67
Puzzle 70

Puzzle 65
Puzzle 68
Puzzle 71

Puzzle 66
Puzzle 69
Puzzle 72

SOLUTIONS

Puzzle 73

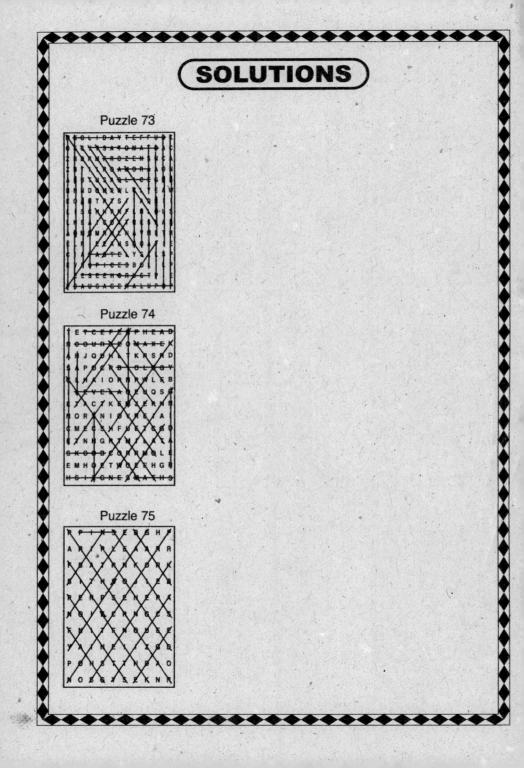

Puzzle 74

Puzzle 75